EARLY ANCESTRY AND EVOLUTION

OF THE HIGHER PLANTS

P.J. Faulks

3

Published by Douglas McLean

at

THE FOREST BOOKSHOP

32 Market Place, Coleford, Glos. GL16 8AA

First Published
1983

Ⓒ *P.J. Faulks, Parkend, Glos.*

ISBN 0 946252 07 6 Hardback
ISBN 0 946252 08 4 Paperback

Printed in Great Britain by
Logos Ltd.
Typesetting by 'Soluna' Typesetting Service

CONTENTS

INTRODUCTION

In 1879, Charles Darwin wrote in a letter to Joseph Dalton Hooker of the Royal Gardens, Kew, "The rapid development, as far as we can judge, of all the higher plants within recent geological times is an abominable mystery".

The higher plants referred to comprise about 250,000 modern species of flowering plants or angiosperms arranged in about 400 families. Fossils of former higher plants are not found with certainty in rocks older than about 135 million years, corresponding to the end of the Jurassic Period.

Yet among the Lower Cretaceous fossils there have been found a few which can already be referred to modern families of higher plants. When the Upper Cretaceous is reached, many of the fossils can be referred to modern families. Correspondingly, many ferns and gymnosperms are common fossils in the Lower Cretaceous, but by the Upper Cretaceous they have been replaced almost wholly by those of higher plants. No wonder that Darwin, whose theory of evolution was based on the selective value of small continuous changes exerted over long periods of time, considered this to be an abominable mystery.

Thus there is an apparent contradiction: there is no unequivocal fossil record of higher plants stretching back into the Jurassic or Triassic Ages and yet identifiable fossils of higher plants are found in the Lower Cretaceous. An attempt will be made in this dissertation to resolve this apparent contradiction and show that the higher plants have a considerably longer history than that which is currently envisaged, and that this history has an important bearing on their present structure and variability.

In order to do this, it was necessary to start with a reconsideration of the principles of evolution and to trace the consequences of this into the taxonomy of the higher plants and the interpretation of their floral structures.

CHAPTER I

THE CONTEXT OF EVOLUTION WITH SPECIAL REFERENCE TO THE HIGHER PLANTS.

THE MEANING OF THE TERMS 'IIIGHER PLANTS' AND 'EVOLUTION' IN THE PRESENT CONTEXT.

THE NATURE OF EXISTENCE AND DESCENT.

THE EVOLUTION AND MANAGEMENT OF THE SEXUAL PROCESS.

THE RELATIONSHIP BETWEEN GENOTYPE AND PHENOTYPE.

ASPECTS OF PHENOTYPIC EXPRESSION.

THE CO-EXISTENCE OF ADAPTIVE AND NON-ADAPTIVE CHARACTERS.

THE ORIGIN OF NON-ADAPTIVE CHARACTERS.

THE UNIQUENESS OF NODAL PHENOTYPIC DOMAINS.

Before presenting a formal theory of evolution which is to be applied particularly to the higher plants, it is necessary to discuss terms and to state the context in which the theory is held to operate.

THE MEANING OF THE TERMS 'HIGHER PLANTS' AND 'EVOLUTION' IN THE PRESENT CONTEXT

In Europe in the 18th century, at a time when it was widely accepted that the earth had come into existence by divine creation as the home of a specially created mankind, it was naturally thought that all other living creations should also have some degree of importance in a divine hierarchical scheme. It would seem that Linnaeus himself had this sort of idea in mind when he gave the name 'Principes' to the class of Palm Trees (a name still used today in some countries). So it came about that plants such as mosses were considered to be 'lower plants', and flowering plants or angiosperms to be 'higher plants'.

With the advent in the 19th century of notions of evolution, it was assumed that the 'higher plants' were 'higher' because they were 'more highly evolved' than the 'lower' or more primitive plants. In Darwin's own words (Darwin, 1875), "And as natural selection works solely by and for the good of each being, all corporeal and mental endowments will tend to progress towards perfection"—it being understood, of course, that mankind represents the pinnacle of perfection.

Others later carried this notion a stage further by postulating that those plants which had, among other things, simple flowers (such as *Magnolia*) were more primitive than those which had more complicated or 'advanced' flowers (such as *Taraxacum*). The notion of the flower of *Magnolia* as the simplest or most fundamental type was put forward by Goethe (1790) in pre-evolutionary-theory days: in due course it was but a short step to its being considered as the most primitive.

A final step was the assumption that the more 'primitive' plants were the ancestors of the more 'advanced' plants. Much effort has since been expended on the construction of 'Family Trees' (or better, perhaps, Trees of Families or Orders) which suggest how, beginning with an Order of primitive plants (usually Magnoliales, as the 'trunk'), other less primitive Orders were subsequently derived (as the larger 'branches'), then others still less primitive (as the smaller 'branches') and finally the least primitive (as the 'twigs').

The above mentioned notions of primitiveness and evolutionary change will be the subjects of examination in the following pages.

The noun 'evolution' in its original general sense was used to describe the emergence of each event in turn in a chronological series (as a parallel to the revealing of a series of subjects depicted on a scroll which is being unrolled). In its early biological application, it was given the meaning of the derivation by descent during geological time of new kinds of organisms from their ancestors. Later still, the verb 'to evolve' was used to describe specific derivation as in 'B evolved from A'. In the later 19th century, both words unfortunately acquired the meaning of 'improvement with successive derivation'.

Derivation implies genetic change from generation to generation. However, change can take place at different rates, so it is necessary to consider not only kind of change but also rate of change with time.

The fossil record shows that change during descent is not, in fact, a simple continuous process. *Types* of organisms (for example, Trilobites and Calamitales) show discontinuity in that they appear 'suddenly' and flourish for many millions of years and yet, within these types, there is a succession of *variants*. There is, however, no general evidence of one type changing *gradually* into another, though the variants may succeed, or even more or less merge into, one another.

The discontinuity between types has sometimes been 'explained away' by geological or cosmic catastrophe which supposedly wiped out former types so thoroughly that there could be no resurgence, and allowed new ones to proliferate. The possibility must be borne in mind that this is not correct, and that there is some more generally applicable biological explanation, such as is made later in this dissertation.

THE NATURE OF EXISTENCE AND DESCENT

That the nature of individual plants and the nature of their environment are such that the plants exist may be expressed by saying that the plants and the environment are congruous. The word 'congruous' has here been chosen as a *neutral* word to express the notion of 'successful conjunction' of plant and environment without implying any causes for such successful conjunction. (A new verb meaning 'to achieve mutual successful conjunction' would be a useful addition to the English language: there are several colloquial verbs in current usage, but they are unsuitable for adaptation.)

It may be noted that the essence of achievement and maintainance of congruity throughout the life cycle is the simple continuous passive fitting together of plant and its immediate environment. How plants arrive at or achieve congruity in the course of evolution is the subject of the next Chapter and can conveniently be referred to as the Congruity Theory of Evolution.

The environment referred to above consists of everything external to an individual plant throughout the whole life cycle. In a modern flowering plant this includes the style and stigma in which the pollen tubes grow and the endosperm which encloses the developing embryo: as will be noted in due course, these features are of the greatest importance in the evolution of the higher plants.

Plants have descendants, and these have other descendants and so on over an extended period of time: there is thus possible a serial history of congruity. However, the operation of the sexual system of reproduction precludes simple linear descent and ensures that the usual table or diagram of pedigree is a reticulum.

Examination of the table of pedigree extended over thousands or millions of generations would reveal (judging by the nature and behaviour of modern plants) the following characteristics:

11

Termination of descent. (No vertical lines of descent proceeding from certain individuals. Termination defined as failing to produce pollen or ova.)

Proliferation and extenuation of descent. (Increase or decrease with time of the number of vertical lines proceeding from individuals.)

Restriction of hybridisation *between groups* of individuals. (Reduction in the number of and, later, the elimination between groups of the lateral connections which represent sexual union. The table of pedigree of groups which show serial discontinuity would have a branching structure, as isolated groups themselves divide into further isolated groups. It would be of the greatest importance, from the point of view of choice of a theory of evolution, to note whether the branching structure of the table was like the usually depicted 'evolutionary tree' with trunk dividing into large branches, these into smaller branches, and so on, or whether it was more like the equivalent of numerous adventitious stems arising simultaneously from a rhizome, or something partaking of both arrangements.)

Restriction of crossing between individuals *within a group* isolated as above. (Lateral connections selective, that is, some sexual unions allowed and some disallowed.)

If the genotypes of all the individual plants entered in the table of pedigree could be known, it would be possible to come to statistical conclusions concerning the workings of the table. However, the data can never be available to do this, so it is necessary to construct a theory of evolution which will consistently account for all the characteristics of the table of pedigree such as proposed above.

THE EVOLUTION AND MANAGEMENT OF THE SEXUAL PROCESS

It will be appreciated from what has been said in the previous section concerning hybridisation and crossing, that the sexual process is so involved in general evolution that it is necessary to note its own evolution and management.

The sexual process (meiosis with chromatid segmental interchange and fusion of gametes) occurred very early in the history of the plant kingdom as an innovation which was preserved because segregation and recombination provide for new combinations of genes, hence for greater phenotypic variability and the possibility of congruity with new environments.

After the advent of gametes, innovations which led to the protection and direction of the gametes were preserved because they economically enabled full advantage to be taken of the sexual process. Hence arose various kinds of gametophytes.

Since the zygote is diploid, it is automatically more complex than either of its component gametes. Such innovations that led to the advent of a sporophyte generation would therefore be preserved. Following that, such innovations that led to the protection and direction of spores and gametes (and hence the simultaneous atrophy of the gametophyte generation) would also be preserved.

Since protection and direction are more easily provided separately, innovations leading to heterospory (and the separate treatment of microspores and megaspores) would be retained. The emergence of the higher plants was now able to take place. In these, protection is provided principally for the megaspore and female gametophyte (which became parasitic within the body of the sporophyte) and direction principally for the pollen (through various agents of pollination) and for the pollen tubes (by chemical direction in the stigma and style). The management of the sexual process now became necessary.

The first aspect of management concerns the maintainance or improvement of the direction of the microspores. Some higher plants retained the original pollination by wind, but others diversified into pollination by insects, water, etc., as they invaded new habitats and new opportunities presented themselves.

The second aspect of management concerns the prevention of hybridisation between more or less distinct populations of plants, and hence the avoidance of loss of adaptation through disruptive introgression. This is accomplished by a fertility block (cross-fertilisation not possible or, if possible, sterile offspring produced).

The third aspect of management concerns the maintenance of stability (in character and numbers) within populations delimited by sterility block: the equivalent genetical equilibrium is sometimes referred to as homeostasis. Most higher plants acquired bisexual flowers in the course of evolution as the most economical arrangement for reproduction. However, self-fertilisation as a consequence of bisexuality may lead to undesirable segregation of characters. This has therefore been counterbalanced in the course of evolution by the acquisition of mechanisms which maintain suitable genetic combinations. Two processes are involved, namely selective mating and differential proliferation by the genotypes produced by that selective mating. A range of mechanisms provides selective mating: examples are, different times of ripening of stamens and stigmas, mechanical arrangements to keep certain pollen away from certain stigmas, different degrees of abortion of stamens or ovaries, pollen incompatibility controlled by multiple alleles, and cytoplasmic male sterility.

It is interesting to compare the management of the sexual process among animals, especially vertebrates, with that among the higher plants.

The first aspect is similar in that there is transfer of the sexual cells, but different in several other respects:

—the animals themselves provide the necessary mobility.

—there is recognition and acceptance for mating of like animals (as within 'species').

—since animals are dieecious, there is also recognition of and stimulation to acceptance by the opposite sex through some form of sexual dimorphism (as in form, colour, odour, sound or behaviour).

—there is the further recognition of, and mating preference for, members of the same local or micro-race (and antagonism against other local races). This leads to the isolation of local races so that they tend to be given the status of 'species': the equivalent in higher plants would merely be that of varieties. The mechanism of isolation may partly account for the remarkable diversification of such perceptive creatures as birds and insects, and to a lesser extent for the diversification of mammals. It is the basis of human tribalism and hence of race formation.

Although plants cannot directly exercise recognition, it should be noted that indirect or surrogate recognition is possible and indeed has been of importance in the speciation of the higher plants. The perceptiveness of an insect pollinator will lead to mating of plants which are alike in some special respect: hence such plants and their pollinators will tend to become genetically isolated. In some cases this has led to remarkable interdependence as exemplified by *Yucca*, *Ficus* and many Orchidaceae and their pollinators. In the latter, the flowers of some have even come superficially to resemble insects. Should the insect fail, the only means of survival would be the adoption of self-pollination: this would explain the occurrence together of insect-resemblance and the self-pollination of some orchids, and also possibly the ploidy which could have facilitated the change (by altering the expression of self-sterility factors).

(In passing it may be noted that, among insects, even more complex surrogate recognition obtains in the evolution of mimicry.)

The second aspect is similar in that animals have fertility blocks between more or less distinct populations, but different in that there is reinforcement of blocks by recognition and rejection of members of other 'species'.

The third aspect is somewhat different in that, since animals are dioecious, all offspring are crossbred. Nevertheless, there may still be the need for the prevention of too close inbreeding, by the adoption of, for example, systems of polygamy with their corollary of encouraged or enforced exogamy (by expulsion of rival males). Some animals may thus be similar to some plants in being sensitive to inbreeding depression. Systems of mating are controlled by the recognition of, and antagonistic stimulation by, members of the same sex.

Among animals there is, however, a fourth aspect, which is absent from plants, namely some degree of choice, by individuals, of mating partner(s) within recognition-groups or combinations of recognition-groups. This makes possible the acquisition and maintenance of those means of recognition mentioned in the other aspects of management of the sexual process referred to above. Various genes, but particularly major genes of high penetrance and also sex-linked genes, are involved in choice by *individuals* and hence, statistically and in the course of time, with the *general* development within inbreeding groups of the various particular means of recognition.

It will have been noted from the above paragraphs that mutual recognition of members of a group and preference for mating within the group have been the cause of much subdivision of animal phyla. Darwin (1874) wrote much on individual choice of mating partners, but it appears that he did not appreciate the fundamental importance of a theory of group recognition.

THE RELATIONSHIP BETWEEN GENOTYPE AND PHENOTYPE
ASPECTS OF PHENOTYPIC EXPRESSION

Evolution is concerned with the serial congruity of genotypes which change from generation to generation. However, genotypes are not directly subject to being proved for congruity, but their corresponding phenotypes are. The way in which phenotypes express genotypes will therefore have an influence on acceptance or otherwise of genotypes for congruity.

It is here proposed, in what can conveniently be referred to as the Theory of Dual Control of Inheritance, that there are two independent aspects of expression and that both are necessary to explain the facts of evolution.

In the first aspect, it is postulated that there is restricted expression of the numerous genes concerned with basic structure and function. The genes are presumably polymorphic, but whether this is so or not cannot be investigated by Mendelian methods.

All living organisms are integrated physico-chemical systems, the integration being expressed in growth, structure and function. In a complete range of theoretical genetical combinations (as in a factorial universe) a certain domain of combinations may be used to produce organisms which have a smaller phenotypic variance than that which the genetic domain would theoretically generate if there was no restriction on expression.

Dobzhansky (1941) long ago suggested that species were stable because of special co-adaptation of their genes. However, if there is co-adaptation of the genes this must lie, not in the static genotype but in the expression of that genotype, that is in the phenotype. If the phenotype is more or less fixed by physico-chemical necessity, it will be formed by any genotypes which provide a minimal essential assemblage of genes, even though the total genotype, of which they form a part, could be different from what might be predicted on a one-gene one-character basis.

In nature, therefore, we could expect to find distinctive stable types of plants corresponding to preferred or nodal phenotypic domains. We do, in fact, find such distinctive types, and they have persisted for many millions of years.

An important part of evolution is accordingly concerned with the emergence of nodal phenotypic domains. After emergence, these domains accumulate genetic variability, and ultimately this becomes available for the emergence of new domains, and so on.

This brings us to the second aspect of the expression of the genotype, in which it is postulated that there are other genes concerned with the modification of the aforementioned basic structure and function of the plants of the nodal phenotypic domain such as to produce a multitude of variations.

THE CO-EXISTENCE OF ADAPTIVE AND NON-ADAPTIVE CHARACTERS

The Darwinian view of adaptive characters is given in his summary of *The Origin of Species*, as follows:

"But if variations useful to any organic being ever do occur, assuredly individuals thus characterised will have the best chance of being preserved in the struggle for life: and from the strong principle of inheritance, these will tend to produce offspring similarly characterised. This principle of preservation, or survival of the fittest, I have called Natural Selection. It leads to the improvement of each creature in relation to its organic and inorganic conditions of life: and consequently, in most cases, to what must be regarded as an advance in organisation. Nevertheless, low and simple forms will long endure if well fitted for their simpler conditions of life."

On the other hand, there have been expressions of the alternative view.

Thus, Cronquist (1970, p.240) gives among other examples, ". . .the adaptive significance of the characters which mark the Myrtales as a group is obscure. Some botanists have thought to see survival value, in such characters as epigyny and loss of endosperm, but tetramerous flowers and simple, opposite leaves pose greater difficulties, and internal phloem still escapes the most valiant attempt at a Darwinian interpretation."

If it can be accepted that the plants of a nodal phenotypic domain exhibit what can conveniently be called whole-plant congruity, their general characters considered separately will appear to have little or no biological meaning. On the other hand, within some sub-divisions of the domain, some characters will often be found to be capable of adaptive interpretation. The nearer a subdivision is to the original phenotypic domain the less likely are its general characters to be adaptive. Thus, the Myrtaceae will show more adaptive characters (as, for example, xeromorphism) than the Myrtales. Species will show greater adaptation, and ecotypes greatest of all. It is the variability within the species, in fact, which allows continual adjustment to environment to be made.

THE ORIGIN OF NON-ADAPTIVE CHARACTERS

It is now desirable to provide a theory to account for nodal phenotypic domains and their non-adaptive characters.

Hitherto, biologists have tended to regard action as proceeding from structure. Such a notion has been greatly fostered by classical Mendelian genetics, in which certain characters of organisms are said to be produced by certain genes.

It is here proposed, however, that structure proceeds from action since the properties of matter are such that, in physico-chemical systems (such as plants), out of all sequences of events which are supposedly possible, only certain autonomic reflex sequences of chemical action (and hence of growth, development and function) would, on full mathematical and thermodynamic analysis of material and energy balances respectively, be found to be actually possible. In other words, the *essential* plant is not a structure but an abstract function of matter, which can be called an Autonomous Reflex Gene Activation Programme (ARGAP).

Just what the earliest chemical reactions were in the formation of the organic matter which led to the evolution of living things is not known with certainty. At some stage, simple sequences of reactions would have become possible in the first organic matter. Reflex sequences would then have become possible whereby Chemical A_1 induced the formation of Chemical B_1, this in turn induced the formation of A_2 and this in turn B_2, and so on until B_x induced A_1 and the cycle was repeated. The next step would have been that the functions of the A's and the B's would have become specialised to stimulative and directive respectively . If the A's and the B's were (or allowed the formation of) protein and nucleic acid respectively (as stimulatory cytoplasm and directive gene store) these could then be said to constitute the first 'organism', and the cyclic reflex reaction sequence which gave rise to it to constitute the first ARGAP. New ARGAP's would have come into operation from time to time by saltation as the gene store became by accident complex enough to allow them to operate. In turn, these ARGAP's would have allowed the evolution of more complex organisms, then cells and then more complex cellular structures which finally culminated in the modern plants.

The relation between an ARGAP and a gene store would explain why a *Lens* cytoplasm can satisfactorily provide the initial stimulus to enable the ARGAP to develop a *Vicia* plant from a *Vicia* nucleus introduced into the *Lens* cytoplasm by an abortive fertilisation, and why some development can be obtained from much more bizarre combinations obtained by artificial implantation of nuclei into foreign cells. The ARGAP and the basic phenotype would be identical for *Lens* and *Vicia* but the respective gene stores would provide for the appropriate modification of the basic phenotype.

The relation would also explain why polyploidy would not generally prevent the operation of an ARGAP, for it would not upset the selective activation of the genes but would actually stabilise the process. This would seem to be borne out by the very high chromosome numbers of ancient types of plants such as *Equisetum* and *Ophioglossum*.

If the theory discussed above is correct, it is possible to account for the non-adaptive characters of the plants of nodal phenotypic domains. The characters produced by a particular ARGAP would perforce be integrated but would not necessarily be individually adapted to some particular feature of the environment. The only requirement would be that the whole-plant should be congruous at the time of the emergence of the nodal phenotypic domain. Adaptive characters may be later superimposed, but the value of these may be obscured as further and different adaptive characters are acquired, and so on.

(In further support of the theory, it may be noted in passing that the utilisation by an ARGAP of only a certain portion of the total genotype in the development of the phenotype may account for the remarkable uniformity of mules obtained as crosses of male donkeys and highly variable female horses, and for the restricted range of phenotypes in segregates from fertile interspecific hybrids of *Nicotiana* (Anderson, 1939).

THE UNIQUENESS OF NODAL PHENOTYPIC DOMAINS

It is here postulated that emergences of *successful* nodal phenotypic domains have been rare events. Certainly it would appear from a count of the main groups of plants and animals that there have been relatively few in the history of the world.

This would argue against the emergence of identical domains. On fossil evidence there is no reason to suppose that the domain of the higher plants is not unique. Further, in spite of the differences between mono-cetyledons and dicotyledons, the similarities between them are so great that it is likely that both belong to one domain. That domain has become subdivided so that there are now about 250,000 sub-domains as modern species. Although this is large in comparison with the numbers in some other groups of plants, it is small compared with a possible 700,000 for insects.

The fact that domains can split into several hundred thousand sub-domains over periods of 100 - 300 million years and still retain their original basic characters, suggests that whatever controls their fundamental pattern of development is not material, for that would surely be subject to change.

An ARGAP would, however, have been able to provide the necessary control indefinitely, for it would be incorruptible. Modification would be able to ring the changes repeatedly on the basic phenotype. On this analysis, insects will continue to give rise to insects and with an evermore increasing number of subdivisions in their classification—apart from the minute possibility of the advent of a new ARGAP taking over and giving rise to an as yet unknown class of animals.

It should be noted that a particular ARGAP, since it is a function of matter, would operate wherever its environment was suitable. It would produce the same basic phenotype in all parts of the universe from the beginning to the end of time. It is theoretically possible that, could they be brought together from the depths of space, the members of these independent domains would (modification permitting) even be capable of interbreeding. Such possibilities could go far to reconcile the views of creationists and evolutionists. It would appear that the creation of matter and the endowment of that matter with the property of self-organisation, are inseparable.

It is interesting to speculate how many ARGAP's have been operative in the sequence leading to the existence of the higher plants. I think it is likely that the number is in units rather than in tens, and even then only in the low units, say perhaps five. It could be about the same for mammals as for the higher plants. It would be helpful if ultimately it became possible to construct mathematical models of ARGAP's and of the process of saltation from one ARGAP to another.

CHAPTER II

THE CONGRUITY THEORY OF EVOLUTION

THE NATURE OF THE GENOTYPE

THE DOMAINAL GENE STORE

THE NON-DOMAINAL GENE STORE

THE EVOLUTIONARY CYCLE OF THE GENOTYPE

EMERGENCE OF A NEW DOMAIN

THE GENERATION OF VARIABILITY

SELECTION AMONG THE GENOTYPES OF A POPULATION

THE DELIMITATION OF SUB-DOMAINS

REPETITION OF THE CYCLE OF SUB-DOMAIN EMERGENCE

EMERGENCE OF A NEW AND DIFFERENT DOMAIN

CHANGES OF GENOTYPE OCCASIONED BY SELECTION IN THE GENE STORES

EFFECT OF SELECTION IN THE DOMAINAL STORE

EFFECT OF SELECTION IN THE NON-DOMAINAL STORE

EFFECT OF JOINT SELECTION IN THE DOMAINAL AND THE NON-DOMAINAL STORES

THE TAXONOMY AND PHYLOGENY OF THE PRODUCTS OF EVOLUTION

Evolution is concerned with the serial achievement of congruity. Congruity is a function of environment and genotype. It is necessary, therefore, if evolution is to be explained, to state what is postulated concerning the nature of the genotype, the way it changes with time, and the results of change.

THE NATURE OF THE GENOTYPE

It is postulated that the genotype contains two gene stores, the domainal and the non-domainal, each with its own behaviour.

THE DOMAINAL GENE STORE

The domainal gene store is that which is operated on by the ARGAP to generate the basic phenotypic organism.

If any part of the genotype of a modern plant is to be put forward as an identifiable domainal gene store, it is the heterochromatic parts of the chromosomes. It would appear that all parts of the heterochromatin would have some function, since nullisomics of non-polyploids are inviable.

It is postulated that the genes of a domainal store are highly replicated. This would allow *modulation* of the action of the ARGAP, in that the duration of action and amount of product may be varied. It is also likely that there is further modulation by co-activation of genes (which can be called assimilatory genes) linked in the store with the ARGAP-operated genes. Modulation would control general size, habit and vigour of the resulting plants.

In some kinds of plants, particular domainal sub-stores (identified by position on particular chromosomes) may vary so much from chromosome to chromosome that certain pairs of variants are necessary as a minimum in the zygote to provide adequate conditions for the modulated development of the phenotype. In such plants, artificial inbreeding leads to loss of vigour called inbreeding depression: as would be expected, such plants have efficient cross-pollination mechanisms.

THE NON-DOMAINAL GENE STORE

The non-domainal gene store could be identified with the euchromatic parts of the chromosomes. At least some of its genes would be major genes of high penetrance.

The non-domainal genes would be activated by the activity of the domainal genes after they in turn had been activated by the ARGAP, and their activity would *complement* the expression of the domainal genes.

Modulation and complementation would together lead to the modification of the expression of the basic phenotype.

An interesting corollary to such arrangements is that, if the basic pattern of development results from the operation of an ARGAP (the effect of which will be most evident in the embryological and early life of an organism), and the features of the mature organism are largely due to modulation and complementation, it follows that ontogeny will appear to repeat phylogeny.

THE EVOLUTIONARY CYCLE OF THE GENOTYPE
EMERGENCE OF A NEW DOMAIN

If, in a certain domainal gene store, suitable basic variability accumulated, the gene store could then be used for the operation by a different ARGAP. The new ARGAP would most likely act on the zygote, since that cell would be in the most favourable condition to allow a new kind of development. The phenotype produced by the new ARGAP would possibly appear not much different from that of its parents, but its potential would be different. It would, from the beginning, be modulated by the nature and content of the domainal gene store used in its formation. The takeover by a new ARGAP and the emergence of a new nodal phenotypic domain is likely to be a rare event.

The plants of a new domain would have to exhibit whole-plant congruity with the environment in which they emerged but, if they had new potential for modulation, their subsequent adaptive proliferation could be rapid and extensive.

THE GENERATION OF VARIABILITY

Generation of variability between plants in the next generation (where such variability is subject to selection) takes place by change in kind and amount of genetic material and its redeployment in the cells of the present generation (where the variability is not subject to selection, since it occurs only in parts of the plants).

If diversifications occur in somatic cells which do not ultimately give rise to sexual organs, they are lost. However, those which occur in primordia which give rise to flowering shoots may ultimately enter the gametes. A whole shoot may be 'mutant', so that the plant becomes a chimaera, but this is unlikely to upset the congruity of the whole plant.

The function of all types of diversification noted below is the generation of variability which, on selection, leads to changes in the gene stores and hence to changed phenotypes.

Diversification At Gene Loci

Changes at gene loci can take place at any time in the life cycle from zygote onwards to gametes. Changes at loci include:

Loss of activity of genes.
Modification of activity of genes.
Formation of new types of genes (from 'spare' reduplicates of other types of genes).
Gene multiplication by polyteny and tandem reduplication.

Diversification of the Nature and Disposition of Parts of Gene Stores

It is possible that non-domainal genes may on occasion be assimilated by the domainal store, or domainal genes by the non-domainal store. More information is needed on the origin and evolution of the two types of store before further discussion on such transfer.

However, if the domainal sub-stores are identified with the hetero-chromatic parts of different chromosomes, it would appear that they are fairly stable and, since crossing-over rarely takes place in them, they could vary independently. After some time, one identifiable sub-store could have many variants in a population of plants (as if they were an indefinite series of related but different 'supergenes'), and they would be selectable through the resulting phenotypes which contained them.

Diversification of Chromosome Complements of Somatic Cells

Changes in chromosomes either before or at mitosis result in cells which have:

Increased numbers of chromosomes by breakage, or decreased numbers by fusion.

Chromosomes altered by translocation, interchange and inversion.

Altered numbers of chromosomes due to failure of, or irregular, mitosis.

Altered numbers of accessory chromosomes due to irregular segregation.

Diversification of Genetic Constitutions of Chromosomes at Meiosis

Chromatid segmental interchange at meiosis leads to new combinations of alleles of different kinds of genes in the non-domainal store, and of new combinations of altered sub-stores in the domainal store.

Diversification of Chromosome Complements of Gametes

Failure of meiosis leads to unreduced ova and pollen, and irregular meiosis to unequal segregation of chromosomes.

Diversification of the Genotypes of Zygotes Through Sexual Fusion

This diversification takes place because the number of different com-binations of pairs of genotypes of gametes is usually greater than the number of different genotypes of gametes.

SELECTION AMONG THE GENOTYPES OF A POPULATION

Selection for termination takes place among the genotypes of a popu-lation, and for the differential proliferation of the survivors. It can take place at any time in the life cycle, from the zygote onwards. It may be due to random causes (drift) or to systematic causes (advantage or dis-advantage in achieving congruity).

Since variability is continually generated, selection continually occurs so that taxonomic differences arise between the original population and that of its descendants. The new population of descendants may differ in many ways from the parental one: in the simplest case it may differ merely in gene frequencies, or, in a more extreme case, by a whole set of chromosomes (as when a tetraploid replaces the parental diploid, the latter becoming extinct).

Taxonomic differences can also arise between sub-populations of descendants. These differences may be related to:

—Geographical fragmentation leading to the formation of two or more isolated sub-populations, which then change independently of one another.

—Ecological preference whereby different genotypes occupy environmental climes or more-or-less discontinuous ecological areas or niches. This will involve some restriction on cross-fertilisation and genetic exchange, and hence will promote independent change in the descendants and so give rise to distinct sub-populations.

—Cross-fertility genetic block, such as imposed between diploids and some derived polyploids.

(Note that among animals, but not among plants, there is here an additional category of sub-population isolated by recognition of and preferred mating among the members of a local race—see Chapter I, 'The Evolution and Management of the Sexual Process'.)

Although selective change continually takes place, it must be noted that both kind and rate of change vary considerably with time. This has extremely important consequences for the *pattern* of evolution, as will be explained in Chapter III.

THE DELIMITATION OF SUB-DOMAINS

If a sub-population is successful, then those innovations which lead to its delimitation will be retained.

Judging by the present large number of sub-domains (as modern good species) in the higher plants, sub-populations have a tendency to become permanently delimited.

Sub-populations long separated from one another either do not hybridise together or do so with reduced fertility, or sterile progeny are produced. The ultimate cause of this fertility block in terms of enzymology or other physico-chemical activity is not clear.

It is also not clear how far positive selection of genotypic mechanisms is involved. It cannot be involved where sub-populations have merely been separated by distance, for in this case the sub-populations must change independently. That such changes are slow is indicated, for example, by the fact that *Corozo oleifera* (Giseke, 1792) of South America and *Elaeis guineensis* (Jacq.) of Central Africa, the common ancestors of which were divided by continental drift perhaps up to 90 million years ago, still cross readily when brought together by human agency (and so belong merely to different sub-species, not to different genera).

At the other extreme, a polyploid may be totally infertile with its parental diploid(s) by the nature of the process involved and from the moment of its inception.

However, where the separation of the sub-populations is of ecologic origin and does not involve either simple distance or polyploidy, it is likely that innovations which lead to positive delimiting mechanisms would be retained under conditions of environmental stability so as more readily to maintain congruity by preventing introgression.

Bearing all of the above in mind, some more or less proximate conditions which tend to delimit sub-populations are listed below in order of increasing degree of restriction of cross-fertilisation and hence more stringent delimitation:

1. Pollination between adjacent sub-populations may be evaded by their acquisition of, for example, different flowering dates or different specialised insect pollinators. However, plants of the sub-populations would breed together successfully and produce fully fertile progeny if crosspollination accidentally occurred.

2. If pollination does take place and offspring are formed, they may be sterile. Pollen and ova of offspring, if formed, are non-viable. Non-viability is often associated with irregular meiosis but, even when meiosis is more or less regular, the chromosomes may not pair properly.

3. Pollination and fertilisation may take place, but the zygotes or embryos abort. Abortion may be due to chromosome unbalance, the action of lethal genes in the embryo, inhibition by the endosperm, or undetermined causes.

4. Pollination takes place and the pollen tubes at least start to grow, but the tubes and gametes are defective or inadequate in some way so that fertilisation does not take place.

5. Pollination takes place but the pollen does not germinate on the stigma, there being some positive rejection between pollen and stigma. (This is not to be confused with incompatibility operating within inbreeding populations.)

When the stage of pollen rejection is reached, the sub-populations can be said to have the status of sub-domain. The sub-domain will be as independent as the original domain. Even though it is generated by the same ARGAP, its modulation will be different, and its members will tend to show more adaptive characters when its isolation has been of ecologic origin. (In terms of modern plants, a sub-domain would be what is termed a 'good species'.)

REPETITION OF THE CYCLE OF SUB-DOMAIN EMERGENCE

If fully delimited sub-domains are equivalent in genetic structure to their original domains, it could be expected that they, in turn, would be subject to the processes of generation of variability among their members, followed by genetic selection and the delimitation of sub-populations, thus leading to the emergence of further sub-domains. This cycle could be repeated indefinitely.

EMERGENCE OF A NEW AND DIFFERENT DOMAIN

If the genotypes of any member of an ultimate sub-domain ever accumulated the variability which would allow the operation of a new ARGAP and the emergence of a new nodal phenotypic domain, a cycle of evolution would be completed and a new one started.

CHANGES OF GENOTYPE OCCASIONED BY SELECTION IN THE GENE STORES

Changes in the gene stores of a population occasioned by selection among its members, and the corresponding types of changes in phenotypic expression, must now be noted.

EFFECT OF SELECTION IN THE DOMAINAL STORE

It was mentioned, when discussing the functions of the domainal store that, at one extreme, substores could be so variable that only certain combinations of variants of a particular sub-store in pairs of homologous chromosomes would allow full modulation of the phenotype. This introduces the notion of fractionally 'deficient' sub-stores. Suppose that, in a diploid species, Position A in Chromosome Type 1 could be occupied by one of a series of sub-stores in each of which a different part of the sub-store was deficient. Since inheritance is disomic, certain pairs of variants would jointly provide at least the content of one full store, and plants of that constitution would be normal. In the absence of crossing-over within sub-stores, deficiencies in their content could not be remedied but, if the species had obligatory cross-pollination, suitable combinations of deficient sub-stores would make this unnecessary. Differential proliferation would, of course, be necessary to provide for balanced polymorphism of the variants of the sub-stores.

At the other extreme, a particular substore of a species would be invariant and without deficiency. Plants which have such invariant substores could be self-fertilised indefinitely without loss of vigour of the offspring. It would even be possible for an ARGAP to be operative on a haploid nucleus and produce at least a vegetative haploid plant.

In between the two extremes described above, would be found species with moderate variability of particular sub-stores. This leads, in cross-breeding plants, to the possibility of selection for sub-store variants. The plants produced by different combinations could vary considerably in size and habit and possibly also in related resistance to environmental stress. Those plants of a sub-population which occupied a certain ecologic niche would tend to have the same general characters and to breed together. Such plants, having achieved balanced polymorphism with respect to the variant substores, and if morphologically fairly distinct from other sub-populations, would be classified as an ecotype.

The possibility of selection of sub-store variants may explain why some plants, such as *Medicago sativa*, are sensitive to inbreeding. They may already have undergone selection of sub-store variants in the production of their particular current phenotype, and therefore any further restriction on combination of variant sub-stores by inbreeding would lead to intense inbreeding depression.

A corollary to sub-store variant selection in the formation of ecotypes would be that, in some cases, when certain different ecotypes are crossed, the offspring could under suitable conditions be larger and more vigorous than either parent, thus exhibiting what is known as heterosis. This process is copied in artificial systems of combined inbreeding and outbreeding for the production of hybrid seed which in turn produces a crop of extremely vigorous plants, as exemplified by the system used for *Zea mays*.

EFFECT OF SELECTION IN THE NON-DOMAINAL STORE

The genes of the non-domainal store complement those of the domainal store, and their selective retention has enabled plants to achieve, for example:
  —Suitable flower colours for insect pollination.
  —Resistance to pathogens.
  —Suitable modifications of flowers for pollination by particular insects, such as zygomorphy for flowers pollinated by bees.
  —Control of cross-fertility through multiple alleles affecting pollen compatibility and heterostyly.

The smaller inbreeding groups distinguished by characters such as those mentioned above, could be described as 'Mendelian races'.

Knowledge of the occurrence of non-domainal genes which allow plants to achieve, for example, resistance to a particular pathogen, has come about by the relevant genes having two or more alleles. There must, however, be large numbers of invariant genes in the non-domainal store. Some of these genes could well have been polymorphic at some time and have now been reduced to the invariant condition by selection of one allele. Many cultivated plants show in their history the mutation of formerly invariant genes to allelic forms. The presence of a few genes has been discovered by their having a pleiomorphic effect under abnormal circumstances as, for example, the gene which confers resistance in some strains of *Hordeum sativum* to poisoning by the chemical DDT.

The positions in the chromosomes of the non-domainal genes which are polymorphic can be found by calculation from the frequency of crossovers in segregating progenies. The corollary to crossing-over is that both useful new types of genes and also alleles of established types of genes can by this process be combined with those portions of the sub-domainal stores of chromatids which are undergoing selection for the emergence of ecotypes. The ecotypes can thus retain the advantages offered by such non-domainal genes and alleles: this would be particularly relevant to the situation whereby the non-domainal genes control mechanisms for adjusting cross-pollination, and the domainal genes need cross-pollination to provide particular sub-store variant combinations to maintain differential proliferation.

EFFECT OF JOINT SELECTION IN THE DOMAINAL AND NON-DOMAINAL STORES

Although the processes of selection in the domainal and non-domainal stores have been described separately, they would not occur separately. They would in fact tend to overlap or coincide so that their extreme products, the ecotype and the Mendelian race could not be distinguished from each other. Such products would be designated, in terms of modern plants, as sub-species (especially if they had clearly separated provenances) or varieties.

THE TAXONOMY AND PHYLOGENY OF THE PRODUCTS OF EVOLUTION

It has been postulated that, in the process of evolution, inbreeding groups of plants have continually been isolated. Taxonomy is concerned with the recognition of such groups, and phylogeny with the interrelationships of the groups by descent.

The Classes of plants are those taxons which arose as nodal phenotypic domains by the advent of new ARGAP's. The Class of Higher Plants or Angiosperms contains all the modern descendants of one nodal phenotypic domain.

This domain rapidly broke up into sub-domains under the divisive influence of different habitats, geographical separation and ploidy. Divisions, Orders and Families are recognised as containing the modern descendants of these sub-domains, but the dispositions of the Divisions, Orders and Families cannot be decided on without a theory of phylogeny. Darwinian theory would have it that the taxons run in chronological sequence:

Class - Division - Order - Family

In the scheme presented later in this dissertation, some case will be made for the chronological sequence to be:

Class - Family

Divisions and Orders would then merely be groups of collateral Families.

The sub-domains of which the modern descendants are grouped as Families would have become serially further divided into sub-domains, the penultimate sub-domains in the series being recognised as modern Genera, and the ultimate sub-domains as Good Species.

Beyond the Good Species lie a multitude of quasi-isolates:

Species (other than Good Species)
Sub-species
Sub-sub-species
Microspecies
Varieties
Races
Biological races
Physiological races
Chromosome races
Strains
Micro-races
Geographic species
Clines
Variants
Mutants

Of these, some are Good Species in the making, and some are not. Of the latter, some apomicts and interchange hybrids are undoubtedly isolated and have been listed as species, but they are not isolated in the manner defined for Good Species and they are not isolated in the manner defined for Good Species and they therefore cannot be included in that category.

Although it might be very interesting from the evolutionary and phylogenetic points of view to have a catalogue of Good Species, it would not be a practical proposition to attempt to construct such a catalogue. The categories given above will therefore continue to be used, and the context will provide the distinction from Good Species.

CHAPTER III

GENERAL APPLICATION OF THE CONGRUITY THEORY TO THE EVOLUTION OF THE HIGHER PLANTS

THE DISCRIMINATION THEORY OF THE EMERGENCE AND SUCCESS OF THE HIGHER PLANTS

THE CONGENITUM THEORY OF THE FORMATION OF EVOLUTIONARY ISOLATES

THE BREAKUP OF THE DISCRIMINALES

THE DELINEATION OF CONGENITA

THE NOTION OF DIRECT DESCENT OF MODERN FAMILIES OF HIGHER PLANTS FROM GYMNOSPERMS

THE BREAKUP OF CONGENITA

THE FURTHER DEVELOPMENT OF CONSTRICTA AND THE FORMATION OF SPECIES

SUMMARY OF THE PROCESSES OF EVOLUTION OF THE HIGHER PLANTS

THE DISCRIMINATION THEORY OF THE EMERGENCE AND SUCCESS OF THE HIGHER PLANTS

It is here assumed that the ancestors of the modern higher plants emerged as a nodal phenotypic domain. These ancestral plants were presumably technically gymnosperms, but had far greater potential for adaptation than those from which they were immediately derived.

However, if modern higher plants are compared with modern gymnosperms, the only consistent features that the higher plants have and the gymnosperms do not, are special areas of tissue for the reception and germination of pollen, and the embryo-sac with double fertilisation and associated formation of endosperm.

It would appear, therefore, that the ancestral plants had some special feature (denied to the ancestors of the modern gymnosperms) which led to their remarkable proliferation.

Interestingly, the above mentioned consistent differences probably have a common biochemical involvement, namely that of self/non-self discrimination (the equivalent, either in chemical mechanism and/or effect, of the control of immune reaction in animals). If, by innovation, immune reactions were at least temporarily relaxed in the ancestors of the higher plants, it would be possible to explain why the higher plants developed certain specialised structures and spread so rapidly over the earth. Arguments may be put forward as follows.

1. The immediate result of immune reaction relaxation or suppression would have been to permit wider outcrossing than usual among diverging sub-populations and so increase the potential for new genetic combinations for the operation of selection for congruity.

2. Relaxation would make it possible to allow or encourage pollen to be received by, germinate on, and grow in special receptive areas (stigmata), and so allow plants to exploit the advantages of closed ovaries in the protection of ovules and the dispersal of seeds (by opening at maturity, by becoming fleshy and edible, etc.). Apparent relaxation may be due in fact to the ability of pollen to overcome immune reaction at the stigma. Some faint evidence which might support this sort of interpretation is the existence of widespread parasitism among such angiosperms as have secondary growth, and the known possibility of making vegetative grafts between plants of supposedly remote affinity, both situations being quite different from those which obtain among gymnosperms.

3. Relaxation would make it possible to evolve double fertilization. Two nuclei of the ovule could be fertilized by two gametes from the pollen grain without post-fertilization immune reaction interference, and so allow the evolution of various types of embryo sac as found in angiosperms.

4. Relaxation would allow the non-rejection of embryos in their parasitism on the ovule parent. Endosperm from the fertilized secondary nucleus would envelop the developing embryo. The endosperm may

well have had a function parallel to that of the mammalian placenta, namely immune reaction suppression between the developing embryos of wider crosses and the nucellus of the ovule parent.

It would appear possible therefore, that a single cause, namely a change in immune reaction control, could account for both an outburst of variability and the evolution of the special features of the higher plants or angiosperms.

Since it would appear possible that all that was necessary to start the rapid evolution of the higher plants was certain genetic variation in the control of immune reaction or self/non-self discrimination, I propose to give the name 'Discriminales' to the hypothetical nodal phenotypic domain the plants of which had, or had the potential for, such variation.

THE CONGENITUM THEORY OF THE FORMATION OF EVOLUTIONARY ISOLATES
THE BREAKUP OF THE DISCRIMINALES

After the Discriminales had spread over a wide area, its members would inevitably have tended to become divided into primary inbreeding subgroups.

From the point of view of evolution, one important point about this process is that the formation of any subgroup would isolate it from all others. Its genetic inheritance would be likely to be unique, for probability would be against any two or more subgroups achieving congruity with environment in exactly the same way. It would have its own particular size, combination of characters, variability and potentials for future change.

The other important point about the process is that, if as postulated, a change in control of self/nonself discrimination allowed wider outcrossing, then the Discriminales could have become very widespread and clinally diverse before breaking up into inbreeding subgroups. The result of this would be that it would become possible for a large number of subgroups to be formed more or less simultaneously, a process perhaps unique (as judged by the large number of families of the higher plants) in the history of the plant kingdom.

The production of a large number of independent subgroups would be made particularly easy by any geological upheavals which led to changes in the kind and number of new habitats.

It is in fact here suggested that the number of subgroups formed was several hundreds, possibly more than the number of usually accepted modern families of higher plants.

I propose to use a new name 'congenitum' to denote an original or primary inbreeding subgroup and all its descendants. (The word 'phylum' is already in wide use, principally in relation to the animal kingdom and to borrow it for the subgroups herein described may lead to ambiguity.) It is inherent in the nature of a congenitum that all its modern species must be related by descent, and their inter-reations must also be capable of being investigated in the absence of fossils by the methods of neontological phylogeny.

The formation of evolutionary isolates in the manner described above can conveniently be referred to as the Congenitum Theory.

The above scheme may now be compared with that of classical phylogeny in which a Darwinian 'advance in organisation' leads from gymnosperm to primitive angiosperm and this in turn to primitive dicotyledons and primitive monocotyledons and each of these two groups divided again and again to arrive at advanced orders or families.

An example of a portion of such a tree of evolution is shown below, that of Takhtajan (1959) quoted in Engler (1964).

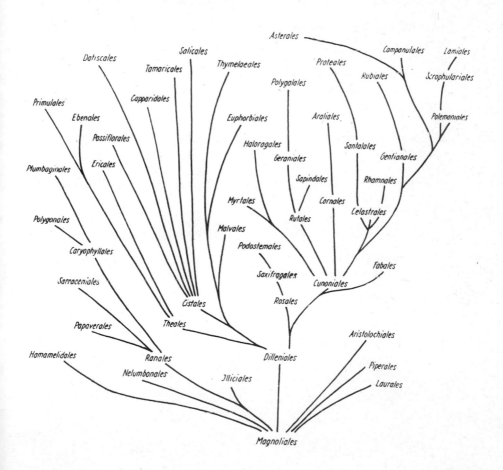

A feature of such trees is that they purport to show the derivation of 'advanced' modern orders from 'primitive modern orders, but the processes of such transformations are not made clear. Another feature is the derivation from order to order in multiple steps, a process which would not be compatible with the geological history of the higher plants.

Even without further analysis, such features make it impossible to accept phylogenetic trees assembled in this way.

THE DELINEATION OF CONGENITA

The congenita would have been formed fairly early in the life of the Discriminales. Some of them would have died out after various periods of time. Others would have survived and varied greatly in their subsequent development so that at the end of the process one congenitum may contain only one modern species whereas others may contain many—up to thousands in extreme cases.

The task is to assign all modern species to their respective congenita. Fortunately, almost all of this task has already been accomplished in the assembly of modern species into genera and families, for in many cases it is clear that the family constitutes the modern members of the congenitum. In fact, the fairly ready division of modern species into families provides strong support for the Congenitum Theory of more or less simultaneous subdivision of the Discriminales into congenita.

As envisaged, there would be correspondence between the following and their respective congenita:

1. Various small families or sections of families which have sometimes been given family rank, e.g., Punicaceae, Simmondsiaceae, Gunneraceae, Paeoniaceae, Grossulariaceae, Kingdoniaceae, Asparagaceae. There has been a tendency among taxonomists to make tidy classifications by combining these groups with larger ones.

2. Some well-recognised sections of larger families which have distinctive genomes or karyotypes, e.g., Bambusoideae, Pomoideae.

3. Various distinct families, especially the more homogeneous ones such as Magnoliaceae, Labiatae, Typhaceae, Orchidaceae.

4. Some Orders, provided they are homogeneous, e.g., Salicales, Proteales, Cactales.

The principle would be to make groups as distinct as possible using all sorts of available data. The size of any group would be limited by the requirement that all its members could feasibly be related by direct descent.

THE NOTION OF DIRECT DESCENT OF MODERN FAMILIES OF HIGHER PLANTS FROM GYMNOSPERMS

It is implicit in the Congenitum Theory of the development of the higher plants from the Discriminales that changes took place with the passage of time independently in each congenitum. If this is so, then it must be contemplated that every congenitum had, and every derivative family has, a direct line of descent from gymnosperms—even such 'advanced' families as Campanulaceae and Orchidaceae.

Readers will, of course, find it difficult at first to accept the sequence of, say,

Gymnosperm → Discriminales → Congenitum Campanulacearum
→ Campanulaccae,

as a complete and separate evolutionary sequence. However, it is certainly easier to contemplate such a sequence than one which involves the usual distant Magnoliaceous ancestors, followed by numerous 'derivations' until the 'advanced' Campanulaceae are at last reached.

Again, it may be protested that such very peculiar plants as orchids could not possibly have evolved directly from gymnosperms. On the contrary, to my mind it is the peculiarities themselves which argue in favour of such an origin.

The Orchidaceae are a homogeneous family which might almost be considered monogeneric. They fall at most into half a dozen tribes approximating to 'good' genera. The first members of their congenitum were almost certainly some sort of humus-plants and acquired their special mycorrhizal habit early in their history. They also acquired insect pollination: the forms of insects and orchid flowers presumably evolved together, so that matching proliferation has resulted in about 20,000 species of orchids. These have been grouped into 600 or more genera, but these genera are for taxonomic convenience only and hybridisation easily crosses generic boundaries. It has sometimes been suggested that the Orchidaceae had their origin in the Amaryllidaceae, but there are no likely ancestors to be found in that family, heterotrophic or otherwise, as might be expected if the Orchidaceae were at the end of a long evolutionary sequence of specialisation.

Taking all things into consideration, if the Orchidaceae do not have a simple direct line of descent from gymnosperms, then the alternative must be through complicated hypothetical phylogenies which pose far more problems than those they purport to solve. This principle can be extended to apply to all other families of the flowering plants.

THE BREAKUP OF THE CONGENITA

The course of events following the formation of a congenitum would be that its member plants themselves would begin to differentiate and separate into inbreeding groups. Again, the determination of the composition of these groups would be partly by systematic effect and partly by chance, so they would show considerable genetic variation.

Even as soon as the equivalent of modern sub-species or ecospecies began to form, there would be the possibility of hybridisation with the formation of polyploids. Such raw polyploids would have a better chance of survival if they were longer-lived perennials, and their offspring would have the ability to occupy new ecologic niches.

There would thus arise within a congenitum various inbreeding groups, some diploid and some polyploid. Further modification of polyploids would become possible through chromosomal segregation, introgression, secondary hybridisation and secondary polyploidy. Further, some diploid ancestors of polyploids may die out: in a changing environment their lack of ability for environmental congruity would lead to their extinction. It would appear that diploid perennials are less capable of congruity than the polyploids derived from them. However, a change from perennial habit towards biennial or annual habit allows diploids to exploit a number of ecological niches (such as continually disturbed soil or areas of extreme drought broken only periodically by rain or flood) denied to normal mesophytic perennials. Diploid annuals which subsequently become polyploid can adopt self-fertilization and thus partially fix successful genotypes.

At the end of this stage the inbreeding groups within a congenitum would be virtually isolated genetically and would consist of:

—Various diploid groups, some of which may have given rise to polyploids. These diploid groups would tend to consist of shorter-lived plants.

—Various polyploid groups, some primary and some secondary. They would tend to consist of longer-lived plants.

There is no evidence of subsequent *general* increase in *degree* of polyploidy. Presumably the sterility barriers rise too sharply to allow general hybridisation between high polyploids and, in addition, the offspring of such unions tend to be weakly.

Since polyploidy tends to prevent further outbreeding—it may be thought of as a 'bottleneck'—I propose to give the name 'constricta' to all the aforementioned inbreeding groups (even though some of them do not contain polyploids) as a matter of convenience for reference and partial description. Thus the primary subdivisions of the Discriminales are the congenita and the secondary subdivisions are the constricta.

The modern descendants of a constrictum will be those corresponding to the subdivisions of a family known as sub-families, tribes, sections or even perhaps good genera.

THE FURTHER DEVELOPMENT OF CONSTRICTA AND THE FORMATION OF SPECIES

In the formation of congenita and constricta, the main genetic themes were established. During subsequent ages, many variations on those themes came into existence, so that at the present time there are about 250,000 species. It is natural, therefore, that change and divergent subdivision of constricta due to sporadic variation and selection over long periods of time should be called speciation. It is what is referred to by Darwin in his *Origin of Species,* for he did not deal with the emergence of new domains or with their initial subdivision into congenita and constricta.

Speciation has undoubtedly been promoted by the successive formation of new ecologic niches in the course of geological time, not only by geological and climatic upheavals but by the influence of new faunas, in particular the insects and the herbivorous mammals.

What happened in the distant past can only, of course, be conjectured. However, some indication has been obtained by the study of the effects of the Ice Ages with respect to recent prehistory, and by the study of the effects of the destruction of forests and the spread of agriculture in historic times.

The word 'species' is used to denote a group of modern individuals which have a common sexual behaviour and therefore have sufficient genetical stability to allow the group to be described and named. Species which conform more clearly to an exclusively inbreeding group are sometimes called 'good species': it was no doubt such recognisable groups that John Ray (1653) had in mind when he described a species as having *"Distincta propagatio ex semine".* Besides these, there are many species named for convenience in taxonomic reference, and which have a less well-defined biological identity.

The variations on a genetic theme and their taxonomic treatment may be illustrated by what Le Maout & Decaisne (1872, p.622) wrote of the Labiatae, a family which is currently described as having 200 genera and 3,200 species. "The Labiatae form one of the most natural groups of plants: the characters of its members are so uniform that it may be called monotypic, as if all the species could be comprehended in a single genus, and the discrimination of its genera is hence very often difficult. For the same reason the affinities of the Labiatae are but few."

It is not possible to give names to all the groupings which lie between an early constrictum and its modern derived species. There may be 0, 1, 2, 3, etc., stages and these cannot necessarily be discovered by taxonomic methods, for parallelism will lead to improper association.

The grouping proximate to the species is, however, normally called the 'genus'. The genus name and the species name together make up the taxonomic name of a plant.

It should be noted that, although a family may contain a large number of genera and species, it is not necessary to postulate a large number of stages to account for the number of species, for the numbers of subdivisions at each divergence will have been multiplicative.

The large numbers of current species of higher plants would seem to Darwinists to be an embarassment that needs to be explained away. Thus, Huxley (1942, p.389) says, ". . .while it is inevitable that life should be divided up into species as units of organisation, the number thus necessitated is far less than the number which actually exist. Species formation constitutes one aspect of evolution, but a large part of it is in a sense an accident, a biological luxury, without bearing upon the major and continuing trends of the evolutionary process."

However, according to the Congruity Theory of evolutionary change, there is no *a priori* reason why genotypes of widely different origins should be precluded from becoming compatible with a given environment: there is no 'necessity' for one genotype of one origin to fill one environment exclusively. In fact, the existence of a vast number of species lends support to the theory of variously achieved congruity. The "major and continuing trends of the evolutionary process" mentioned by Huxley, reflect the Darwinian notion of evolutionary 'progress' which, on the present theory, is discardable.

SUMMARY OF THE PROCESSES OF EVOLUTION OF THE HIGHER PLANTS

PHASE 1. *Acquisition of potential*

In this phase there is the emergence of a nodal phenotypic domain, the members of which have great potential for new developments, including outcrossing and the resulting increase of selective introgressive variability, the formation of closed ovaries, and the acquisition of xylem vessels and sieve tubes. The ancestral group called the Discriminales is thus formed.

PHASE 2. *Migratory thrust*

There follows a migration of the Discriminales to occupy a wider and more varied territory. Geographical isolation and regional environments then lead to the more or less simultaneous breakup of the Discriminales into numerous inbreeding groups called congenita.

PHASE 3. *Boosted thrust*

In response to more local environmental conditions there is now a breakup of congenita into variable numbers of inbreeding groups called constricta.

The shorter-lived plants tend to remain diploid.

A considerable boost is given by polyploidy to longer-lived plants in their ability to occupy new niches. Increase in size and/or variation in form allow the development of herbaceous perennials, shrubs, trees, climbers, lianes and epiphytes. The former vegetation of the world is suppressed: new lianes and epiphytes smother the ferns and gymnosperms, and the irregularly spreading branches of the new trees penetrate the symmetrical crowns of the gymnosperms.

PHASE 4. *Occupation tightened*

A great number of different types of higher plants of various origins ensure that variation is adequate for them to provide some congruity with changing environments, particularly with changing local environments. The dominant position of the higher plants acquired in Phases 1, 2, and 3 is everywhere maintained: they occupy almost every nook and cranny.

Phases 1, 2 and 3 occupy a relatively short period of geological time (less than 10 million years?). The breakup of the Discriminales into numerous congenita and these in turn into numerous constricta allows the higher plants to burst forth and occupy the whole world. The natural consequence of release of constraint on variability as proposed in the Congenitum Theory is the rapid development of the higher plants: there is no room here for Darwin's 'abominable mystery'.

Phase 4 by contrast occupies a long period of geological time (well over 100 million years) with likely extension far into the future. There is evidence that the processes of speciation are such as to provide continuity of occupation in spite of all the destructive efforts of mankind. There may be fewer species in the future, but those that do survive will acquire an even greater resistance to destruction, as is demonstrated by the kind of vegetation which occurs on the increasingly vast areas of cut-over, grazed, burnt, ploughed, dessicated and eroded land in the world.

CHAPTER IV

PRELIMINARY CONSIDERATIONS IN THE RECONSTRUCTION OF THE EVOLUTION OF THE HIGHER PLANTS

FOSSILS AND RELICTS AS AIDS TO RECONSTRUCTION

INTERPRETATION OF THE FOSSIL RECORD OF THE HIGHER PLANTS

THE EARLY DIFFERENTIATES OF THE DISCRIMINALES

EARLY GENERALISED PLANTS AND THEIR EVOLUTIONARY DEVELOPMENT

THE BEARING OF PARALLEL EVOLUTION ON GENERALISED ANCESTORS

THE SALIENT FEATURES OF THE EARLY DISCRIMINALEAN PLANT

THE POTENTIALS OF THE DISCRIMINALEAN PLANT

THE HABITAT OF THE EARLY ANCESTORS AND ITS BEARING ON THEIR EVOLTION

THE NATURE OF THE EARLY HABITAT

THE EARLY MIGRATION FROM SWAMP FOREST

FOSSILS AND RELICTS AS AIDS TO RECONSTRUCTION
THE INTERPRETATION OF THE FOSSIL RECORD OF THE HIGHER PLANTS

The early investigators of the Cretaceous fossil flora, notably Brongniart, recorded that angiosperms similar to modern types suddenly appeared in the Lower Cretaceous and had become dominant members of the flora in the Upper Cretaceous.

Later in the 19th century, after emergence of the idea of evolution and the rationalisation of the process of evolution as due to the action of natural selection, it was noted that fossils of plants such as might have been acceptable as the primitive ancestors of the angiosperms were absent from Jurassic and older rocks. It was the reported sudden appearance of modern angiosperms in the Cretaceous, without the expected intermediate predecessors, that Darwin found so disturbing.

Some botanists, for example Arnold (1947), have accepted the proposition of sudden appearance as something peculiar to the angiosperms.

Others, such as Seward (1931) have suggested that the sudden appearance is deceptive. Concerning some Lower Cretaceous stems and leaves Seward says that ". . .they are old only in the geological sense and astonishingly modern in their anatomical features. They confirm our belief in the antiquity of the angiosperms, antedating by many millions of years, probably several geological periods, the first appearance of the recognisable pioneers of the present ruling dynasty in the modern plant world."

Axelrod (1952) agrees with Seward's belief in an extended history and, by comparison with the evolutionary behaviour of groups such as the ferns, suggests that the angiosperms antedate the Lower Cretaceous by 40 - 50 million years. He explains the lack of fossils by supposing that the early angiosperms were more or less woody plants of tropical uplands: the ancestors of at least the dicotyledons would have been magnoleaceous trees. Although fossils of these were formed in upland lake deposits, such sites would have been vulnerable to denudation in the course of geological time, and the early fossils thus lost. After a period of evolution in the uplands, the angiosperms descended to invade the areas of gymnosperm/fern flora which dominated the damp lowlands. These invaders were fossilised in the lowland sites and hence appear fully evolved in such sites and preserved there since they are not so liable to destruction by denudation.

There is, however, an alternative to Axelrod's scheme. It is here postulated that the ancestors of the higher plants could have been small—even insignificant—plants of lowland floras and not necessarily abundant. Although their remains would undoubtedly be present in fossil deposits, they would not be well enough preserved as to be recognisable. There must have been many small types of plants in the evolutionary history of the plant kingdom: some idea of them is suggested by *Miadesmia,* a lyco-podiaceous spermatophyte of the Upper Carboniferous, which had a vegetative body reminescent of *Selaginella* and was possibly epiphytic.

According to the theories herein presented, they did not give rise to one primitive kind of angiosperm which then gave rise to several others less primitive and so on until the descendants became abundant enough for several fairly 'advanced' kinds to turn up as fossils of roughly the same age. On the contrary, the plants could have acquired potential (as the Discriminales) and then spread and diversified with unparalleled rapidity in the formation of their congenita and constricta about the beginning of the Cretaceous period.

THE EARLY DIFFERENTIATES OF THE DISCRIMINALES

Although it is unlikely that fossils of the Discriminales will be found, it may still be possible to get an idea of what their earlier derivates looked like. The following argument suggests how this could be done.

There is an important corollary to the scheme of formation of congenita, namely that the earlier and more completely polyploidy arose in a con-genitum the more genetically isolated its members would have become. In the limit, polyploid formation and the loss of diploids would lead to the formation of a congenitum of which the modern descendants would con-stitute a single genus only. Some monogeneric modern families such as the Coriariaceae, Empetraceae, Myricaceae, Cercidiphyllaceae and Plata-naceae possibly arose in this way.

The formation of a single-genus family is of course the extreme case. In the more general case where polyploidy is more and more delayed in different congenita, there would be a progression towards small families such as Juncaginaceae (4 genera), Buxaceae (6 genera), Magnoliaceae (10 genera) and onwards to somewhat larger families such as Bignoniaceae (120 genera). But note that the progression does not necessarily extend to larger and especially more herbaceous families for in these there are large numbers of genera of mainly taxonomic convenience.

The earlier a genus was formed, the greater would be the length of time available to it to migrate to suitable niches in other parts of the world. The Coriariaceae and some other small families have wide distributions. Such distributions, although they have disturbed some plant geographers, nevertheless usefully suggest the early genetical isolation of the ancestors. For example, Good (1964, p.70) writes, "As shown by their maps. . .the distribution of Myricaceae and Buxaceae are in differing respects, particu-larly anomalous and inevitably cause a doubt as to whether these families as thus comprehended are really complete natural groups." There may, after all, be a grain of truth in Willis' (1922) propostions concerning age and area.

Although the above mentioned relicts tend to be alike in their simple leaves and small simple greenish flowers, the fact that they are still somewhat diverse indicates that a projection from them to the plants of earlier geological time is still necessary, and will involve the use of other ideas and evidence.

EARLY GENERALISED PLANTS AND THEIR EVOLUTIONARY DEVELOPMENT

THE BEARING OF PARALLEL EVOLUTION ON THE GENERALISED STRUCTURE OF ANCESTORS

In earlier geological time, the ancestors of the higher plants would have had to be even less specialised structurally and physiologically than the previously discussed relictual polyploids if they were to be easily capable of transformation into such varied types as herbaceous annuals and perennials, lianes, shrubs, trees, etc. Evidence in favour of the existence of such less specialised ancestors is provided by parallel evolution in the higher plants.

According to the Congruity Theory it would be expected that congenita and constricta would develop those features which promoted congruity with contiguous environments, and according to the Congenitum Theory they would have to develop them independently and therefore in parallel. This is apparently what did happen, as evidenced, for example, by the evolutionary development of sieve tubes.

Evolution of sieve tubes is from sieve cells with oblique plates (as in gymnosperms) to sieve cells with transverse plates joined end to end to form tubes (as in angiosperms). Eames and MacDaniels (1947) state: "The sieve-tube type is not constant in families or sometimes even in genera. The primitive type is found in some families considered to be advanced, such as the Caprifoliaceae, and the most advanced type occurs in such primitive families as the Moraceae and Ulmaceae. Evolutionary advance in sieve-tube type has apparently taken place within families (Fagaceae, Rosaceae, Leguminosae) and within genera (*Fraxinus, Prunus*). Although the sieve-tubes of vines and herbs are usually of the highest type, all types occur in woody and herbaceous forms."

The acceptance of such parallel evolution allows the Discriminales to be thought of in terms of the most generalised ancestors of the higher plants. These generalised ancestors would undergo parallel development independently in numerous congenita. There is no need to postulate evolution by advance and reversal (perhaps even a sequence of several advances and reversals) as would be made obligatory by accepting the much-branched evolutionary tree of orders or families. The probability of the occurrence of such advances and reversals would be too low to allow them to be accepted as the basis of evolution.

THE SALIENT FEATURES OF THE EARLY DISCRIMINALEAN PLANT

It was mentioned above that the Discriminales would have comprised relatively simple plants such as could diversify directly into more complicated ones without the prior need for simplification.

Accordingly, it is suggested that the salient features would have been as follows:

The vegetative body consisted of a branched stem bearing adventitious roots and leaves with buds in their axils.

The stems contained collateral vascular bundles embedded in a ground tissue which was differentiated into a cortex and ill-defined pith. The roots contained a ring of alternating xylem and phloem bundles embedded in a ground tissue. There was no secondary growth.

The leaves consisted of an ill-defined petiole and lamina with forked venation. The vascular supply to each leaf was a single trace from one lacuna.

The vascular tissue of the whole plant consisted of phloem which had oblique sieve plates, and of xylem of which the conducting elements were tracheids.

The plant body was the sporophyte generation. The reproductive bodies consisted of microsporangia and megasporangia borne on stem structures. The plants would have been monoecious or dioecious.

The megaspores and the structures derived from them were embedded in a large fleshy and nutritive nucellus. The megaspores were retained on the female parent.

After fertilization of the oosphere, the nucellus enlarged and the wall enlarged and thickened, the whole structure forming a seed. At the time of shedding, the seed would not have contained a formed embryo and so was neither monocotyledonous nor dicotyledonous.

THE POTENTIALS OF THE DISCRIMINALEAN PLANT

Having described the Discriminalean plant it is now desirable to indicate its main potentials which would have enabled it to become congruous with new environments and so give rise to modern higher plants:

Stems

The stem had a potential for reorganisation and secondary growth.

Of those which did not reorganise the vascular bundles into either a ring or a cylinder, some acquired a cambium in the cortex. This cambium produced whole collateral vascular bundles in ground tissue (as is typical of some monocotyledons).

Of those which did reorganise the vascular bundles into a ring or cylinder, some acquired a fascicular cambium, some a fascicular and also an interfascicular cambium. These types produced normal dicotyledonous secondary growth. In addition (as in members of the Centrospermae), concentric secondary growth took place by the formation of secondary cambia in the cortex.

In the course of time, some more herbaceous types became more woody, and some more woody types became more herbaceous by increase or decrease of cambial activity.

Variation on the above themes produced a great array of growth forms and types, lianes in particular showing a great variety of structure. It would appear that all the different types evolved independently.

Roots

Most plants which acquired dicotyledonous secondary growth in their stems, also acquired secondary growth in their roots, so that the secondary wood of the stem and taproot and also of adventitious roots became continuous.

Leaves

The leaves had great potential for variation. Some became elaminate and the petiole expanded to form a pseudo-lamina with parallel venation, as in monocotyledons. They could have developed into leaves with sheathing bases or non-sheathing, stipulate or non-stipulate, petiolate or sessile, simple or compound, and with numerous styles of primary venation and either cross or reticulate secondary venation.

The vascular supply to the leaves became correspondingly various, with increases in the number of traces per gap (1 or 3, occasionally 2 per gap) and the number of gaps per leaf.

Vascular tissue

The vascular tissue had the potential for the development of sieve-tubes with transverse plates, and the development of xylem vessels. Vessels were sometimes developed in roots only (as in some monocotyledons) but usually in all parts of the plants (as in dicotyledons).

Flowers

The reproductive structures had the potential to develop a perianth and so become what are termed flowers, and to develop inflorescences of flowers. The microsporangia developed into stamens. Plants had the potential to enclose the young megasporangia (ovules) completely in ovaries and to provide a special area (stigma) for the reception and germination of the microspores (pollen). The number of ovules per ovary could be varied from one to numerous.

Seeds

The ovules had the potential to develop in various ways to provide embryo-sacs capable of double fertilization.

The nucellus was normally disorganised with the growth of the embryo-sac: if not disorganised it formed a nutritive perisperm.

The fertilized secondary nucleus of the embryo-sac gave rise in various ways to a nutritive endosperm. The foods stored were polysaccharides (principally starch), protein and fats (glyceric esters). *Simmondsia* stores wax (higher monohydric alcohol ester)—an oddity, but quite compatible with independent development in congenita.

The embryo occasionally retained or reacquired an undifferentiated state, but it normally developed the potential to grow into an embryo inside the seed before the seed ripened for shedding. The embryo normally produced either one or two cotyledons and was capable of storing foodstuffs and/or of absorbing foodstuffs from the endosperm and perisperm.

* * * * *

The main potentials noted above in stems, roots, leaves, vascular tissue, flowers and seeds were realised in various combinations. Many of the combinations were free, but some were associated or were consequential developments of others (as development of the stigma was associated with closure of the ovary).

There were, of course, a great many other potentials, such as the production of trichomes, nectaries, and chemicals such as alkaloids, polyisoprenes and quinones, the ability to modify metabolic pathways to allow water economy in succulents and to adjust reproductive cycle to day length. These and many more were capable of independent development in all sorts of combinations, thus making the higher plants the most varied group in the whole of the plant kingdom.

THE HABITAT OF THE EARLY ANCESTORS AND ITS BEARING ON THEIR EVOLUTION

THE NATURE OF THE EARLY HABITAT

If, as herein suggested, the ancestors of the Discriminales were small unspecialised plants, the environment which they occupied must have been stable and yet favourable to terrestrial plant life.

Places which would fill this specification would be suitable for the development of swamp forest. Geological history shows examples of such areas that existed for millions of years. If favourable to plant life they would have already been occupied by plants other than just the ancestors of the Discriminales: these plants were Filices, Pteridospermae and Lycopsida, which now form extensive beds of coal.

The ancestors of the Discriminales would therefore have occupied a micro-environment within the swamp forest. I suggest that this was shallow water, and that the plants were hydrophytes rooted in the mud but with the upper parts emergent for photosynthesis and sexual reproduction.

THE EARLY MIGRATION FROM SWAMP FOREST

The pro-Discriminales now acquired control over immune reaction. This led not only to the advent of closed ovaries but also to outcrossing and an increase in variability. The development of seeds with a pre-formed embryo, and food stored principally in either endosperm and/or embryo, would have provided an even more flexible life cycle.

The plants could now invade the moist areas of moss forest at higher altitudes and the drier areas of the swamp forest. They could also invade deeper water, running water, brackish water and even the sea. More important still, they could invade areas subject to drought between seasonal floods and so finally spread to areas not subject to flooding and finally even to almost rainless and saline deserts. They could also spread to higher latitudes in which seasonally low temperature would permit only periodic growth.

As the invasion proceeded, hybridisation between ecologic variants gave rise to the larger perennial polyploids of the new flora. At this stage, the formation of congenita and constricta would have been well under way as previously described.

CHAPTER V

THE SPHENOPHYLLUM THEORY OF THE ORIGIN OF THE HIGHER PLANTS

DISTANT RELATIVES OF THE HIGHER PLANTS

In previous discussion it has been suggested that the pro-Discriminales were small gymnospermous spermatophytes. It is now necessary to consider what the ancestors of these plants could have been.

THE SPHENOPHYLLALES AS COLLATERALS OF THE DISCRIMINALES

The Gnetales, Bennettitales, Pentoxylales, Glossopteridaceae, Caytoniaceae and Cycadales have all been put forward from time to time as possible precursors. Their relative merits and demerits have been summarised by Sporne (1971), who concluded that the Cycadales are the most favoured candidate. Even so, the transition from Cycadales to flowering plants would present formidable difficulties both structurally and in process of descent.

With regard to the theory presented here, only the Glossopteridaceae in the above list would appear to be distant enough in time to antedate the ancestors of the Discriminales. Some members of the Glossopteridaceae were small plants, but the organisation of the plant body would appear to be quite different from what has been proposed here as something approximating to an ancestral type. Nevertheless, Melville (1962) has suggested an extensive series of changes which the reproductive branches of *Glossopteris* might have undergone to produce the angiospermous flower.

However, in my opinion there are still better candidates. I should like to draw attention to the Sphenophyllales as possible collaterals of the ancestors of the Discriminales. They have a known history extending from the Late Devonian to the Early Triassic, with the main development during the Carboniferous Period.

The plants have been described as having the habit of a *Galium*. They were even at one time thought to be aquatic with, of course, emergent spore-bearing strobili. They commonly had six leaves per whorl. The stem showed secondary growth in the specimens which have been preserved as fossils.

The reproductive structures, the strolibi, are of particular interest. They are somewhat varied in structure but generally agree in that their building-units were composed of two parts. The lower portion consisted of a barren leaf-like structure and the upper portion consisted of sporangiophores (sometimes bearing sporangia in pairs) which were partly axillary and partly adnate to the lower portion and sometimes themselves expanded and flattened. The lower leaf-like portions I interpret as bracts and the upper portions as *branch* structures borne in the axils of the bracts. For these sporangia-bearing branch structures I propose the name 'sporoclades'. The recognition of the upper portions as branch structures has important consequences for the theory of floral structure which will be worked out in due course.

In the Sphenophyllales so far described, one species is heterosporous and the remainder isosporous, so even at the beginning of the Triassic they were far from being spermatophytes. However, the Triassic and Jurassic Ages would have provided sufficient time for the further development of heterospory and its extension to the seed-bearing habit before the appearance of the higher plants in the Cretaceous.

The Sphenophyllales themselves as described in the literature cannot be considered as possible direct ancestors of the higher plants for they were far too specialised, particularly in their peculiar internal structure. It should be noted, however, that the peculiarities are most evident in the more recent types before they passed out of the fossil record. Nevertheless, the structure of both their vegetative and reproductive organs shows clearly that, if they had had some smaller relatives with simpler vegetative organisation, those relatives would appear to be just what was needed to develop into the higher plants. Unfortunately, it is unlikely that such smaller, simpler relatives would be preserved as recognisable fossils.

Perhaps Hamshaw Thomas (1958) was nearer the truth than he realised when he suggested that fossils of actual or related ancestors might have already been found, but not recognised because of "the persistence of the old ideas on original plant form based on the classical morphology of Goethe."

THE EVOLUTION OF THE PRO-DISCRIMINALES

It is not enough to suggest that the Sphenophyllalean collaterals evolved into pro-Discriminales. The process must be seen to agree with the Congruity Theory of Evolution, and the relationship between plant and environment must be such as to *allow* change and migration to take place.

It is axiomatic that the large trees, such as *Calamites*, of the Carboniferous swamp forest were congruous with their environment. They were, however, too specialised to change with change of environment or to change to invade other environments. They were not on the path of evolution of higher plants, just as, in a different context, large dinosaurs were not in the path of evolution of higher animals.

The small relatives of *Calamites*, some of which have come down to us as the modern Equisetales, maintained congruity in a changing environment by becoming polyploid (2n = 216), long-lived rhizomatous herbaceous perennials. They are still widely distributed in the world over 200 million years later.

We have now to consider the smallest relatives of *Calamites*, the pro-Discriminales. Swamp-forest free-water is partially, sometimes wholly, seasonal. The pro-Discriminales probably evolved their heterospory, their seed habit and an initially short life cycle in response to this seasonality.

An interesting and instructive parallel is provided by the Water-ferns.

There are large flat areas in Australia which are normally hot desert but which are subject to periodic inundation. This is the habitat of *Marsilea nardu*, in which in the course of evolution the sporocarps have enlarged and become food stores so that they have the equivalent function of the seeds of an angiospermous ephemeral. The sporocarps are so large that they used to be collected as a foodstuff by aboriginal Australians.

After the pro-Discriminales had evolved their seed habit, the stage was set for their rapid invasion of the world.

THE SEXUAL EVOLUTION OF THE DISCRIMINALES
THE INVOLVEMENT OF SPHENOPHYLLALEAN ANCESTORS

If the collaterals of the Sphenophyllales are to be considered as ancestors of the higher plants, it is desirable to indicate how the strobili of such plants could be converted into flowers.

The first step is to postulate what could reasonably happen, on the understanding that the original reproductive structure was a strobilus which consisted of modified branches called sporoclades each in the axil of a bract. The structures and changes postulated are as follows:

1. Sporoclades may abort and so leave barren bracts, or bracts may abort and so leave unsubtended sporoclades.

2. A strobilus may be reduced in a series leading to a remainder of several rings (whorls or flat spirals), further to one ring, and finally to a single sporoclade.

3. Various arrangement of heterospory come into existence, for example, —upper sporoclades may be female and bear megasporangia or ovules, lower sporoclades may be male and bear microsporangia or stamens, the strobilus being heterosporous (bisexual).

   —All sporoclades on a single strobilus may be either male or female, the strobilus being unisexual (and the plants monoecious or dioecious).

4. The microsporoclades may be laminar (fully 'webbed' between the sporangiophores) or segmented laminar (by partial webbing) or not webbed between the sporangiophores.
   The microsporangiophores may vary from simple to extremely compound by bifurcation.
   Microsporangia are normally borne in pairs, one each on the two ends of a bifurcated sporangiophore. Normally the two sporangia will become sessile and thus form the loculi of an anther, the anther and its stalk being termed a stamen. Occasionally the sporangia will be stalked and hence the stamens will bear half-anthers.

Normal stamens may vary in their groupings, from fascicles to branched stamens, to single stamens, to more or less infertile stamens and finally to staminodes of various kinds (such as being modified into nectaries).

5. Megasporoclades are laminar and bear ovules on simple megasporangiophores (funicles). An ovary is formed by the enclosure of one or more ovules by the inrolling and sometimes also the infolding of the lamina of the sporoclade, a process which may be termed clathration.

   If the lamina neatly encloses the ovules the resulting ovary will not be crowned but, if the lamina extends beyond the closure at the top, the ovary will be crowned with an epigynous 'perianth' (which may be as small as a rim, or large and laminar). It is of no importance whether the crown is thought to be of the nature of bracts or of floral axis, since no clear distinction can be drawn between them. However, for the purpose of easy description and understanding, the ovary can be said to be adnate to a cup-shaped floral axis.

   A simple ovary may undergo expansion or expansion with pleiomery to form an apparently 'compound' ovary. Expansion will result in a monomeric structure and, depending on the process involved, the whole may have a common roof or 'stylopodium'. The stylopodium may bear either sessile stigmas or stigmatic outgrowths. Expansion may occasionally be followed by premature dehiscence of the fruit, thus giving rise to secondary apocarpy.

   The vascular strands serving the ovules will be variously arranged in the ovary 'walls': the ovules will have various kinds of placentation depending on the nature of the primary ovary and the mode of expansion.

6. Barren whole laminar sporoclades or segments of such sporoclades, as well as the upper portions of fertile sproclades may become components of a perianth. Stamonodes may form a corona. Bracts formed from the floral axis may also be incorporated into the perianth, and normally form the 'calyx'. (Petals formed from barren male sporoclades often have an emarginate apex.)

7. Internodes, between bracts and different kinds of sporoclades, may be modified into disks (which may or may not be nectarial), or elongated to form androgynophores of gynophores.

8. Most modern higher plants have bisexual flowers as the most economical arrangement for sexual reproduction, but it is not known when bisexuality was acquired.

   There may be a few examples of primal dioecism as suggested by the absence of any rudiment of an ovary in the male flower. There are many examples of secondary dioecism and gyno-dioecism.

It is likely that there was no one primal condition, but that bisexual strobili and unisexual strobili (with monoecism or dioecism) were all represented. It is also likely that unisexual strobili or flowers have been converted to bisexual ones by the simple genetical device of unlocking in the male the previously unexpressed potentiality for the development of female structures. This genetical unlocking could have evolved independently many times over (just as the opposite process of secondary genetical suppression of bisexuality has done).

It would appear that the manipulation of sex is easily accomplished by the higher plants. The modern gymnosperms do not show this capability, though the structure of the male flowers of *Welwitschia* is such that bisexuality by genetical 'transfer' of the ovary is only one step away.

THE SPOROCLADE THEORY OF THE STRUCTURE OF ANGIOSPERM FLOWERS

The ways in which the aforementioned components of a strobilus are used to make flowers are so various that it will be best to develop the Sporoclade Theory of floral structure by giving a familiar example and then discussing variants.

The flower derived from a whole strobilus would, in its most complete bisexual form, consist of ebracteate ovaries (each formed by the enclosure of one or more ovules by the inrolling of a female sporoclade) at the top of the axis, ebracteate single stamens (each formed from a single simplified male sporoclade) below the ovaries, ebracteate barren male sporoclades forming a corolla below the stamens, and bracts forming a calyx below the corolla.

It should be noted that the sequence of development of the above mentioned single stamens is from the base to the apex of the strobilus, that is in a centripetal or acropetal succession. If the male sporoclades were not reduced to single stamens or if pleiomery had subsequently increased the number of stamens, the sequence of development would not be centripetal. The sequence of development of stamens on a male sporoclade bearing numerous stamens is from its own base to its apex, but incorporation of that sporoclade into the strobilus-derived flower would make the sequence of their development appear to be reversed when judged *in relation to the strobilus,* and therefore to develop in a centrifugal (basipetal) succession.

The large terminal flower of *Magnolia* could well have been formed from a complete strobilus in the manner described above. There are, however, some flowers which cannot be derived from a complete strobilus, and many which are not terminal but occur in compound inflorescences. Before proceeding, we must therefore consider the origin and nature of compound inflorescences.

THE MODIFIED-STROBILUS THEORY OF THE STRUCTURE OF COMPOUND INFLORESCENCES

The derivation of a compound inflorescence from a strobilus needs only one assumption to be made, namely that any sporoclade borne on a strobilus is capable, since it is a stem structure, of further proliferation.

A sporoclade, instead of becoming sexually differentiated, could itself grow out and form a new strobilus. These secondary strobili could form flowers and so a raceme of flowers would be produced from the original single strobilus. This process could be repeated so that a compound racemose inflorescence would result.

Proliferation could also proceed in an alternative way on the assumption that a sporoclade may branch to provide a middle segment (which could give rise to a strobilus and hence to a flower) and also two lateral outgrowths each consisting of a segment of sporoclade on a stalk (both segments capable of giving rise to strobili and hence to flowers) plus two more lateral segments on stalks, and so on. One original strobilus could thus give rise to a raceme of dichasial cymes of flowers.

Other patterns could also occur, involving a mixture of racemose and cymose branching, and thus account for the complex inflorescences found in modern plants.

Each final branch of the sporoclades of a proliferated strobilus would end in a sporoclade which, in one extreme example, could be a simple sexual sporoclade and develop anthers or ovules or, in an alternative extreme, could develop into a whole new complete strobilus bearing strobili of sexual sporoclades. The simple sexual sporoclade and all the other structures intermediate between it and the complete strobilus of a strobili of sexual sporoclades, can be looked upon as a reduction series. All these 'reproductive units' can give rise to flowers, and therein lies the origin of the complexity of structure of modern flowers.

It would, of course, be possible to produce a simple definition of a 'flower' as 'the product of a single sexual sporoclade'. Most of the structures now called flowers would then have to be called inflorescences. Such apparent simplification would, apart from the drawbacks of altering an established nomenclature, not be biologically sound in that most of the structures we now call flowers have obviously evolved as reproductive units.

By way of illustration, a single sexual sporoclade could give rise to the simplest unisexual flower consisting of, for example, a naked ovary, as in some species of *Fraxinus*: the product of a strobilus of strobili of sexual sporoclades may be seen in the spikelet of flowers of *Festuca*.

The branches of the proliferating strobilus would be subtended by bracts. If these became leafy and assimilatory, the distinction between the reproductive and vegetative regions of the plant would become less and less definite. This would no doubt provide a selective advantage in some plants in that the period of flowering and fruiting could be extended to suit the habitat. Thus, the whole plant of *Stellaria media* is a compound dichasial cyme.

In the course of time, compound inflorescences would become altered in many other ways, particularly those concerned with advantageous arrangements for pollination by different agencies.

VESTIGIAL STRUCTURES IN MODERN FLOWERS

If flowers really came into being by the processes just described, it could be argued that an examination of the course and orientation of the vascular bundles of modern flowers would reveal how this had occurred.

However, this is not necessarily so: it has been postulated earlier in this dissertation that the ancestors of the higher plants were small hydrophytes without secondary growth, indeed with minimal vascularisation, and hence most capable of the organisation of their sporoclade-derived structures without the complications of extensive prior simplification. Indeed, it might be argued that, if the ancestors had not been so plastic, they would never have become angiosperms.

Another feature which favours that argument is that, in modern fruits in their process of growth and maturation, the formation of xylem is longer delayed than that of all other tissues. Such a delay in the earliest stages of flower evolution would have favoured reorganisation. The delay observed nowadays might even be an echo of a previous necessary suppression of vascularisation.

Incidentally, it should be noted that, if the notion of vestigial vascularisation is retained, the Sporoclade Theory rejected and the Darwinian tree of evolution upheld, there would be a considerable tangle of vascular tissue to be explained in an 'advanced' modern flower after multiple 'derivations'.

Lastly, the acceptance of the obliteration of the very early processes of flower formation would not preclude the retention of vestigial structures acquired in the process of speciation at a much later time when plant types had become more fixed. This, indeed, would seem to be a reasonable interpretation of the facts.

EXAMPLES OF FLORAL STRUCTURES INTERPRETED ACCORDING TO THE SPOROCLADE THEORY

Populus

The male flower consists of a simple axis which bears a number of stamens each of which is derived from a single male sporoclade. The female flower consists of a simple axis which bears an ovary derived from a single female sporoclade. In most species the ovary has two parietal placentae, but some species have an expanded ovary with four placentae.

Corylus

The male flower consists of a simple axis which bears two laminar male sporoclades which in turn bear bifurcated stamens. The female flower consists of a simple axis which bears a crowned ovary derived from one female sporoclade.

Quercus

The male flower consists of a simple axis which bears a perianth of barren male sporoclades, and stamens each of which is derived from a single male sporoclade. The female flower consists of a simple axis which bears numerous barren male sporoclades, and a crowned ovary derived from one female sporoclade. The cupule which subtends the fruit is derived from the barren male sporoclades. Occasional bisexual flowers occur. (Perhaps the papillae on the fruit of *Myrica* represent a reduced cupule adnate to the pericarp.)

Urtica

The male flower consists of a simple axis which bears a perianth of bracts, and stamens each of which is derived from a single male sporoclade. The female flower consists of a simple axis which bears a perianth of bracts, and an ovary derived from a single female sporoclade.

Banksia

The flower consists of an axis which bears four laminar male sporoclades, each bearing one stamen, and an ovary derived from one female sporoclade. The laminae of the male sporoclades are partially coherent: if fully coherent the flower would be somewhat reminescent of those of Verbenaceae and Plantaginaceae.

Santalum

The flower consists of a cup-shaped axis which bears on its rim a perianth of bracts, and stamens, each of which is derived from a single male sporoclade. The base of the cup bears an ovary derived from a single female sporoclade.

Polygonum

The flower consists of a slightly saucer-shaped axis which bears a perianth of bracts, and stamens each of which is derived from a single male sporoclade. The base of the saucer bears an ovary derived from a single female sporoclade.

Phytolacca

The flower consists of an axis which bears a perianth of bracts, stamens derived from male sporoclades, and an ovary derived from a single female sporoclade. Pleiomery occurs in the stamens so that the product of a single male sporoclade is more than one stamen. Pleiomery also occurs in the ovary, and this is followed by secondary apocarpy in some species.

Ranunculus

The flower consists of an axis which bears a calyx and corolla of barren male sporoclades, numerous stamens each derived from a single male sporoclade, and numerous ovaries each derived from a single female sporoclade.

Berberis

As *Ranunculus*, but the flower has only one ovary derived from a single female sporoclade. (*Berberidopsis* has an expanded ovary and should perhaps be returned to the Berberidaceae.)

Cinnamomum

The flower consists of a cup-shaped axis which bears a perianth of barren male sporoclades on the rim, and stamens each derived from one male sporoclade. The bottom of the cup bears an ovary derived from one female sporoclade.

Gymnotheca

The flower consists of a cup-shaped axis which bears on its rim a number of stamens each derived from a single male sporoclade. The base of the cup bears an ovary derived from one female sporoclade. The ovary is expanded, with parietal placentation. The ovary is completely adnate to the cup-shaped axis. (The ovary of *Saururus* has axile placentation and shows secondary apocarpy.)

Aristolochia

The flower consists of a cup-shaped axis which bears on its rim a perianth of bracts, and a number of stamens each derived from a single male sporoclade. The base of the cup bears an ovary derived from one female sporoclade. The cup of the axis is adnate to the ovary, and the stamens are adnate to the stylar column. (The flower of *Saruma* is similar except that the ovary has undergone secondary apocarpy.)

Dillenia

The flower consists of an axis which bears a calyx of bracts, a corona of barren male sporoclades, stamens derived from multistaminate male sporoclades (so that their sequence of development is centrifugal) and an ovary formed from one female sporoclade. In related genera the ovary shows complete secondary apocarpy. (The ovary of *Cephalotus* appears to be secondarily apocarpous and more like those of some Dilleniaceae than of Saxifragaceae.)

Sarracenia

The floral structure appears to be similar to that of *Dillenia*.

Papaver

The flower consists of an axis which bears a calyx of bracts, a corolla of barren male sporoclades, numerous stamens each derived from one sporoclade (so that their sequence of development is centripetal), and an ovary formed from a single female sporoclade. The ovary has undergone expansion and bears a large stylopodium. The related *Platystemon* is secondarily apocarpic. The presence of isoquinoline alkaloids in the Papaveraceae does not guarantee a close affinity with the Ranunculales: berberine was first isolated from a member of the Rutaceae.

Brassica

The flower consists of a simple axis which bears a calyx of bracts, a corolla of barren male sporoclades, stamens derived from four male sporoclades (two show pleiomery?), and an ovary formed from one female sporoclade. The peculiar ovary appears to be simply an intermediate stage in expansion between one with two parietal placentae and one with four (as in *Tetrapoma*): the two interpolated narrow barren sections form the replum.

Corylopsis

The flower consists of a cup-shaped axis which bears on its rim a calyx of bracts, a corolla of barren male sporoclades, and stamens each derived from a single male sporoclade. The bottom of the cup bears an ovary derived from a single female sporoclade. The ovary is adnate to the cup of the axis. (The flowers of *Liquidambar* are borne in heads, reduced and secondarily unisexual. The female flowers have a vestigial calyx and abortive stamens. The male flowers are so reduced and crowded that their identity is lost: their stamens thus appear to be borne in 'catkins'. The flowers of *Davidia* have a similar structure and are similarly reduced. Perhaps Engler's Hamamelidineae ((and some Saxifragineae?)) should be more closely associated with the Umbelliflorae.)

Rosa

The flower consists of a flask-shaped axis which bears on its rim a calyx of bracts, a corolla of barren male sporoclades, and numerous stamens each derived from a single male sporoclade. The hollow of the flask bears numerous ovaries each formed from a single female sporoclade.

Saxifraga

The flower consists of a cup-shaped axis which bears on its rim a calyx of bracts, a corolla of barren male sporoclades, and eight or ten stamens each derived from a single male sporoclade. The base of the cup bears one ovary derived from a single female sporoclade, and is more or less adnate to the cup of the axis. The ovary is expanded and dehisces along the 'ventral sutures': in related genera various degrees of secondary apocarpy occur.

Geranium

The flower consists of an axis which bears a calyx of bracts, a corolla of barren male sporoclades, and two whorls of stamens each formed from a single male sporoclade. There are five connate ovaries, each formed from a single female sporoclade, the styles of which are adnate to a prolongation of the floral axis which forms a carpophore.

Impatiens

The flower consists of an axis which bears a calyx of bracts, a corolla of barren male sporoclades, and one whorl of stamens each formed from a single male sporoclade. The ovary is derived from a single female sporoclade, the stylopodium of which allows dehiscence of the fruit only from the base.

Euphorbia

The cyathium is a modified strobilus. The base of its axis produces a cup-shaped structure bearing male sporoclades, each of which consists of a stamen sometimes subtended by a bract. The top of its axis bears three connate ovaries, each formed from a single female sporoclade. The only fundamental difference between the cyathium and a conventional flower is that, in the cyathium, the male sporoclades are not completely reduced to one stamen only.

Ilex

The bisexual flower consists of an axis which bears a calyx of bracts, a corolla of barren male sporoclades, four stamens each derived from a single male sporoclade, and an ovary derived from one female sporoclade and bearing sessile stigmas.

Note: In the Celastrales and structurally similar Orders such as Rutales, Malvales, Sapindales, the gynoecium appears, in different genera, to be either truly compound (connate ovaries derived from two or more female sporoclades) or falsely compound (expanded or pleiomeric derived from one female sporoclade only). Separate styles and stigmas may indicate the former condition, and a stylopodium or occasional parietal placentation (as in *Feronia* of the Rutaceae) may indicate the latter. The difference may have some taxonomic implication but is of little evolutionary significance. The way in which a pseudo-compound ovary develops from a single female sporoclade may help to determine whether the orientation of the ovules is apotropous or epitropous: this is a matter for further investigation.

Euonymus

The flower consists of an axis which bears a calyx of bracts, a corolla of barren male sporoclades, and stamens each derived from one male sporoclade. There are 2 - 5 ovaries, each formed from a single female sporoclade. The ovaries are connate and are embedded in a massive internodal disk.

Siphonodon

As *Euonymus*, except that the floral axis is prolonged above the ovaries.

Scyphostegia

The male flower consists of an axis bearing a single male sporoclade, the latter composed of three connate stamens and a subtending lamina. The female flower consists of an axis bearing a single female sporoclade which gives rise to a naked ovary.

Note: In *Siphonodon*, the ovaries are adnate to the disk, but in *Scyphostegia*, they are free from the disk, although enclosed by it. If in Scyphostegia the male flowers had been further reduced and borne below the disk, the disk-bearing structure would be termed a 'flower', and the female flowers within it would then be termed ovaries.

Elaeagnus

The bisexual flower consists of a tubular axis which bears on its rim a calyx of bracts, and stamens each derived from a single male sporoclade. The base of the tube bears an ovary derived from a single female sporoclade. The tube of the axis is persistent round the fruit.

Malva

The flower consists of an axis bearing a calyx of bracts, a corolla of barren male sporoclades, and numerous pleiomeric stamens derived from five male sporoclades (so that the sequence of the development of the stamens is centrifugal). There is a whorl of connate ovaries each formed from a single female sporoclade.

Cistus

The derivation is similar to that of *Malva,* but the ovary is monomeric from a single female sporoclade and bears a stylopodium.

Begonia

The male flower consists of an axis which bears a calyx of bracts, a corolla of barren male sporoclades, and numerous stamens each formed from a single male sporoclade. The female flower consists of an axis which bears a crowned ovary derived from a single female sporoclade.

Myrtus

The flower consists of a cup-shaped axis which bears on its rim a calyx of bracts, a corolla of barren male sporoclades, and numerous stamens each derived from a single male sporoclade and hence developed in centripetal succession. At the base of the cup is borne an ovary which is formed from a single female sporoclade and which is adnate to the cup of the axis.

Heracleum

The derivation is similar to that of *Myrtus,* but there are five stamens, and the ovary bears a large glandular stylopodium.

Primula

The flower consists of an axis which bears a calyx of connate bracts, a corolla of connate laminar male sporoclades each bearing a stamen, and an ovary derived from a single female sporoclade. (The corolla is seen to develop as outgrowths of the stamens.)

Fraxinus

In *F. excelsior,* the flower consists of an axis which bears two stamens each derived from a single male sporoclade, and an ovary derived from a single female sporoclade. Female flowers consisting of an axis bearing an ovary also occur.

Asclepias

The flower consists of an axis which bears a calyx of bracts, a corolla of laminar male sporoclade bearing epipetalous stamens each derived from a single male sporoclade, and an ovary formed from a single female sporoclade. The ovary bears a large stylopodium which is involved in special arrangements for pollination. Premature dehiscence of the ovary gives rise to incipient secondary apocarpy, but the two halves of the ovary are held together by the stylopodium until after fertilisation. (*Cinchona* of the Rubiaceae shows a similar type of dehiscence.)

Rubia

The flower consists of a cup-shaped axis which bears a rim-like calyx of bracts, and a corolla of laminar male sporoclade bearing epipetalous stamens each derived from a single male sporoclade. The base of the cup bears an ovary derived from a single female sporoclade, and which is completely adnate to the cup. In *Coprosma,* the male flower consists of an axis bearing a tubular corolla, and the female flower consists of an axis bearing a crowned ovary.

Verbena

The derivation is similar to that of *Rubia,* but the axis is not cup-shaped and the ovary is superior.

Taraxacum

The derivation is similar to that of *Rubia.* The unisexual flowers of *Xanthium* parallel those of *Coprosma.*

Alisma

The flower consists of an axis which bears a calyx of bracts, a corolla of barren male sporoclades, stamens each formed from a single male sporoclade, and an ovary formed from a single female sporoclade. The ovary has undergone pleiomery and secondary apocarpy. (In related *Sagittaria,* the stamens are pleiomeric and are therefore developed in centrifugal succession.)

Hydrocharis

The flower consists of a cup-shaped axis which bears on its rim a calyx of bracts, a corolla of barren male sporoclades, and stamens each derived from a single male sporoclade. The base of the cup bears an ovary with parietal placentation and formed from a single female sporoclade. It has undergone expansion and is completely adnate to the cup of the axis.

Potamogeton

The bisexual flower consists of an axis which bears four male sporoclades (each consisting of a lamina bearing one stamen) and four or fewer ovaries each formed from a single female sporoclade.

Tulipa

The flower consists of an axis which bears a perianth of barren male sporoclades, stamens each derived from a single male sporoclade, and an ovary formed from a single female sporoclade.

Tradescantia

The flower consists of an axis, which bears a calyx of bracts, a perianth of barren male sporoclades, stamens each derived from a single male sporoclade, and an ovary formed from a single female sporoclade.

Festuca

The flower consists of an axis which bears lodicules formed from barren male sporoclades, stamens each formed from a single male sporoclade, and an ovary formed from a single female sporoclade.

Corypha

The flower consists of an axis which bears a perianth of barren male sporoclades, stamens each derived from a single male sporoclade, and a monomeric ovary derived from one female sporoclade. (Note: Most palms have unisexual or polygamodioecious flowers, and many are dioecious. In some palms, the ovary undergoes secondary apocarpy, as in *Trachycarpus*. The flowers of some palms have numerous stamens, as do those of the related Cyclanthaceae: it is conceivable that the peculiar scales on the fruits of palms such as *Raphia* represent vestigial barren male sporoclades adnate to the pericarp.)

Iris

The flower consists of a cup-shaped axis which bears on its rim a perianth of barren male sporoclades, and stamens each derived from a single female sporoclade. The base of the cup bears an ovary derived from a single female sporoclade, and which is completely adnate to the cup-shaped axis. (Flowers of similar structure occur in Scitamineae and Orchidales.)

Endymion

The flower consists of a cup-shaped axis which bears on its rim a perianth of barren male sporoclades, and stamens each derived from a single male sporoclade. The base of the cup bears an ovary derived from a single female sporoclade, but there is no adnation and the ovary is free from the cup.

The structure of the flower is intermediate between that of *Tulipa* and *Iris*. Various degrees of cup-formation of the axis, distinctness between cup and perianth, and of adnation between the cup and the ovary occur in the Liliiflorae: taxonomic separation based purely on hypogyny and epigyny may therefore be contrary to phylogeny.

THE BEARING OF THE SPHENOPHYLLUM THEORY ON THE VEGETATIVE EVOLUTION OF THE DISCRIMINALES

The possibilities of vegetative evolution in the Discriminales in anatomy, secondary growth, morphological diversification, etc., are so well described in a multitude of publications that no further comment is needed.

There are, however, some aspects of vegetative evolution specifically related to near-Sphenophyllalean ancestry which are worthy of mention, namely the peculiar basically triarch stele of the stems and the anatomy of the nodes.

ANCESTRAL STEM STRUCTURES IN THE HIGHER PLANTS

The Sphenophyllales had such a peculiar stem structure as to make it unlikely that they were the direct ancestors of the higher plants. Collaterals may have had some less peculiar structure but, even so, it may be asked whether there are any Sphenophyllalean traces left in modern higher plants.

Insofar as ancestral triarchy may be reflected in modern triquetrous stems and/or three-ranked whorled leaves, there would still appear to be a few examples of ancestral influence. In the monocotyledons, three-ranked leaves occur throughout the Pandanaceae and Cyperaceae. In the Alismaceae the flowers are commonly borne in whorls of three in *Sagittaria*. *Allium* of the Liliaceae has triquetrous stems in some species, and in the Palmae *Neodypsis decarii* of Madagascar, the stems are remarkable in being triangular. In the dicotyledons, leaves are sporadically borne in whorls of three in a number of families, for example in *Erica cinerea* of the Ericaceae. This is not an impressive list, but the preponderance of examples in the monocotyledons may point to an underlying cause.

There is a much more interesting aspect to triarchy, namely that it could be the cause of floral trimery in the monocotyledons. Sporoclades are stem structures and would be expected to organise themselves accordingly: if the stems were triarch the flowers might more easily be trimerous.

Trimery was certainly a feature of the monocotyledons right from their beginning. According to the Sporoclade and Discrimination Theories, more or less simultaneous formation of flowers and closed ovaries occurred as a prelude to an outburst of genetic variation and proliferation of the higher plants. We should expect, therefore, to find triarchy more represented in floral structure than in vegetative structure, for the latter would not have been so restricted in its variation so early in the course of evolution.

The fact that the stems and flowers of dicotyledons tend not to show the effects of triarchy is in agreement with the proposition either that the dicotyledons were derived from a different species or that a group of 'monocotyledonous' characters was lost in aneuploidy so that the resulting 'dicotyledonous' plants were much less subject to morphological restraint.

Although the relation between triarchy and floral trimery may be considered tenuous, it must be remembered that such a judgement is made in the context of modern plants. The relation could well have been much closer in the very early history of the higher plants.

LEAF ARRANGEMENT AND NODAL ANATOMY IN THE HIGHER PLANTS

Since the publication by Bessey (1915) of a list of supposed primitive characters, there has been discussion as to whether opposite or alternate leaves are primitive in the higher plants.

If collaterals of the Sphenophyllales were the ancestors of the higher plants, then the original arrangement was neither opposite nor alternate but whorled with very likely six leaves to the whorl.

Relative reduction in the size of four of these leaves and attachment of the reduced leaves to the remaining two larger leaves would have given rise to two opposite stipulate leaves. Complete reduction of four leaves would have given rise to two opposite exstipulate leaves. Longitudinal separation of opposite leaves would have given rise to alternate leaf arrangement.

Assuming that the six original leaves were served by six one-trace stelar gaps, the stipulate leaves would be served by three gaps each and the exstipulate leaves by one gap each. The opposite exstipulate leaves of the Labiatae, for example, are each served by a one-trace gap.

If all the leaves had remained of equal size, the whorled arrangement would have been retained and each leaf would be exstipulate and would be served by a one-trace gap. If the leaves then separated longitudinally the leaf arrangement would have become alternate or, if incompletely separated, they would have become crowded or pseudo-whorled (as in the Lauraceae).

Thus, a Sphenophyllalean ancestry would not only be compatible with modern types of leaf arrangement but would serve at least partially to explain their origin.

CHAPTER V1

THE HIGHER PLANTS EXAMINED IN THE LIGHT OF THEIR EVOLUTIONARY HISTORY

PRIMITIVE FEATURES AND LIVING FOSSILS OF THE HIGHER PLANTS

THE HIGHER PLANTS AS MOULDED BY THEIR HISTORY

THE GEOGRAPHY OF THE HIGHER PLANTS

PHYLOGENETIC TAXONOMY AND SYSTEMATISATION OF THE HIGHER PLANTS

PHYLOGENETIC TAXONOMY WITHIN CONGENITA

THE GROUPING OF CONGENITA INTO ORDERS

THE ASSEMBLING OF ORDERS INTO EVOLUTIONARY TREES

THE DIVISION OF THE HIGHER PLANTS INTO MONOCOTYLEDONS AND DICOTYLEDONS

THE HIGHER PLANTS IN THE CONTEXT OF THE PLANT KINGDOM

COMPARISON OF THE HISTORY OF THE HIGHER PLANTS WITH THAT OF THE MAMMALS IN GENERAL AND MAN IN PARTICULAR

PRIMITIVE FEATURES AND LIVING FOSSILS OF THE HIGHER PLANTS

In a previous section, an attempt was made through the application of the Congenitum Theory to get an idea of what the early higher plants looked like. It is now possible, with the aid of the Congruity, Sphenophyllum and Sporoclade Theories to arrive at a much closer approximation of their appearance.

It would be expected that those plants in the most stable environments would have changed least. We should, therefore, look for 'living fossils' in an aquatic environment. If we do this, we find that *Ceratophyllum* (Ceratophyllaceae) still retains the Sphenophyllalean whorled leaves and forked venation, and *Hottonia* (Primulaceae), *Najas* (Najadaceae), *Ambulia* (Scrophulariaceae) and *Salicornia* (Chenopodiaceae) are basically very little different from *Ceratophyllum*. Traditionally, Ceratophyllaceae has been regarded as a 'primitive' family, Primulaceae as 'advanced' and Najadaceae as 'advanced by reduction' (Hutchinson, 1960).

It is here suggested that the spine-tipped leaves of *Najas* are homologous with those of *Equisetum,* and that the intravaginal leaf-scales are homologous with the small caducous branches borne by *Calamites*. Although such a suggestion may appear to be rather radical, it is quite in keeping with the proposition made on p.35 that the sequence of changes from gymnosperm—or even vascular cryptogam—to modern flowering plant is very short indeed. The leaves of *Najas* and other members of the Helobiae appear to have a different arrangement from those of *Equisetum*: this is due to changes in growth pattern at the nodes as discussed on p.65. Pseudonodes may be formed by unequal development of internodes and these may be associated with anisophylly.

Among land-plants the whorled leaves of *Casuarina* long ago led to the notion of a relationship with the Equisetales, but *Casuarina* was considered to be a primitive oddity and the notion was dismissed. However, there are many land-plants which are not considered to be primitive and which have Sphenophyllalean features. For example, *Galium* (Rubiaceae), *Wilkesia* (Compositae) and *Medeola* (Liliaceae) all show the original whorled leaf arrangement. Although their inflorescences appear to be rather different, the relation to the original strobilus can be traced. The inflorescence of *Medeola* consists of the remains of a strobilus much reduced after initial proliferation (in the related *Paris* and *Trillium* there is even further reduction to one 'terminal' flower). The capitulum of *Wilkesia* is formed from a once-proliferated strobilus, whereas in *Galium* the strobilus has undergone repeated cymose proliferation.*Wilkesia* almost looks as if it could be a *Sphenophyllum* with axillary capitula: it is a remarkably primitive-looking plant in such a supposedly advanced family.

The flowers of *Galium* and *Wilkesia* have long been thought to be 'advanced' as compared with those of *Medeola,* but none is more advanced than any other—they are merely different in having gone their separate ways in their own congenita. If the Darwinian Evolutionary Tree and notions of Advancement through Natural Selection are discarded, the relations between the abovementioned families can be seen in their true perspective, namely that they are all only one step removed from their ancestors which lived in the Carboniferous Age.

THE HIGHER PLANTS AS MOULDED BY THEIR HISTORY

It has been postulated that the ancestors of the higher plants, the Discriminales, were semi-aquatics of tropical swamp forest. They migrated from this habitat to other habitats and in so doing changed their genetic constitutions, their morphology and physiology. Not only did they make migrations but they were largely made by their migrations, so that their present nature reflects their history.

The Discriminales as hydrophytes had only three primary possibilities for diversification, namely to stay in the swamp forest (thus retaining heavy rainfall, high humidity and at least periodic standing water) and by some means gain enough light for photosynthesis, to move out of swamp forest for other aquatic environments, or to ascend from swamp forest to the cooler but permanently wet environment of the moss forest.

After having explored the primary possibilities, a wide range of secondary possibilities would present themselves. The formation of congenita and constricta would largely correspond to the successive stages in exploration. In these processes, the environment so moulded the higher plants that the marks are discernable to the present time on their families and genera. The marks are so clear, in fact, that it would be difficult to explain them on any other basis than that the ancestors of the higher plants were tropical hydrophytes.

These propositions can best be illustrated by a few examples: extention to other families or orders can be made in due course.

1. *Centrospermae*

Of all the plants which left the swamp forest by waterway, the behaviour of those that came ashore in potential salt marsh are among the most interesting and instructive. When the ancestors of the Centrospermae acquired salt tolerance it was natural that they should proliferate in an unoccupied habitat and give rise to a large group of modern families. They have now spread over the world, occupying not only salt marshes but deserts and semi-deserts of all kinds, seashores, grasslands and cultivated land. The acquisition of salt tolerance would appear to have taken place by adjustment of enzyme activity and balance, for plants in various other families have been able to acquire salt tolerance, though the Centrospermae remain the single largest successful group.

In conformity with the open nature of the habitats, many of the plants are xeromorphic herbs and small shrubs, and the flowers are inconspicuous and pollinated by wind.

2. Asclepiadaceae

Even if the hypothesis of ancestral hydrophytes is accepted, it is still often difficult to decide how a particular family evolved. The greater the diversity of the family the more difficult it is to decide, for the data can be read in opposite directions: it could be assumed that climbing plants gave rise to herbs, for example, or *vice versa*. Secondary adaptation may also cause confusion in such a sequence as water plants to land plants to water plants again. The Asclepiadaceae will be discussed for illustration of choice of approach.

This family contains a variety of herbaceous plants (for example, *Asclepias*), climbers (*Hoya*), trees and shrubs (*Calotropis*), specialised epiphytes (*Dischidia*) and succulents (*Stapelia*). Few members occur in cold regions so it is unlikely that early ancestors moved out of the tropics before differentiation.

Most members of the family are shrubby twining climbers, so it could be postulated that these evolved first and that all other types were secondarily derived from them, principally by the formation of herbs which spread beyond the forests and further differentiated, some of them becoming desert succulents.

There is an alternative, however, which is more in keeping with a hydrophytic origin. Some of the herbaceous forms are torrent plants (such as *Pentasacme*). It is suggested that the first stage in becoming dryland plants was to leave the water by growing on wet rocks and progressing from there to dry rocks and so on to dry land. Damp rocks would be clothed with plants of the habit of root epiphytes and sprawling creepers and as such would be able to invade forests. Succulent creepers and herbs would develop among the drier rocky habitats and these would ultimately invade still drier areas, some even penetrating hot desert.

3. Ericaceae, Orchidaceae and Urticaceae

Various modern families made their first move in escaping from the swamp forest by becoming epiphytes, probably as moss-like plants on the bases of gymnospermous trees and then finally ascending to the canopy.

Near water level, resistance to dessication was not necessary but it had to be acquired before full exposure at the canopy became feasible. The evolution of both the Ericaceae and Orchidaceae probably began in this way: their xeromorphism, mycorrhizal saprophytism, insect-pollination and undifferentiated dust-like seeds were early acquired and have since been retained in their descendants which spread to terrestrial habitats.

The Urticaceae would appear to have specialised differently in remaining below the canopy and soon adapting to terrestrial habitats. Their present liking for organic soils, their broader leaves and wind pollination aided by 'explosive' stamens are all possibly related to the original habitat. It is interesting to note that minute moss-like plants still occur in the Orchidaceae (*Taeniophyllum*) and Urticaceae (*Helxine*).

4. Magnoliales and Fagales

Of the plants which migrated to moss forest as a first step towards a wider distribution, the Magnoliales may be contrasted with the Fagales, even though both groups evolved as trees and shrubs in response to the habitat. We do not know what the earliest ancestors looked like for they have died out, though *Myrica* of the Juglandales could give some indication of what the somewhat parallel Fagales at least looked like.

The ancestors of the Magnoliales acquired strobilus-derived flowers suitable for pollination by beetles and so in their formative period tended to 'tie' themselves to the moss forest. Their descendants have naturally tended to favour moist habitats rather than dry, and warm rather than cold: in the Americas, for example, *Lindera* grows in swamp woodland in New Jersey, *Magnolia* in the peat hammocks of Florida, *Nectandra* in tropical forest in the West Indies and *Drimys* in the temperate rain forest of Southern Chile. In accordance with their early moist habitat, the wood of some genera (*Drimys*, for example) never developed xylem vessels for there was no need to develop them. The primitiveness of families which predominantly dwell in tropical forest was noted by Bews (1927).

By contrast, the Fagales acquired flowers in catkins suitable for pollination by wind. This allowed them to migrate to colder and windier climates so that they became the dominant trees of temperate zones and of mountains in warmer zones. The mycorrhizal habit, no doubt acquired in the moss forest, also proved valuable to them in cooler climates. In contrast to the Magnoliales, all of the Fagales have wood which contains xylem vessels.

5. Gramineae and Crassulaceae

Of all plants which are able to make use of a temporary supply of water after drought the Gramineae are among the foremost. They are able to make use of the restricted growing period partly as ephemerals or annuals and partly as drought-resistant perennials which 'burn up' during drought and shoot vigorously as soon as water is available.

These features give a clue to their likely history. They would have evolved as ephemerals on the fringes of swamp forest where availability of moisture was not permanent enough to maintain tree growth. After their establishment as ephemerals, polyploidy would have promoted the perennial habit. The extreme plasticity of the Gramineae then enabled them to migrate to all parts of the world, even to the harshest climates, and so become its foremost dominant family. The acquisition of the hemicryptophyte habit and basal growth of leaves enabled many of them to occupy vast tracts of land (steppes, savannahs, pampas) against the depredations of grazing animals and periodic fires.

The evolution of the Crassulaceae may be compared with that of the Gramineae in that they also probably came ashore as ephemerals on mudbanks. *Tillaea aquatica* is a polyploid which would appear to be well fitted to this role. Just as in the Gramineae, the Crassulaceae became perennials but responded to drought in quite a different way by becoming succulents. This enabled them to attain a wide distribution in the world though in more restricted habitats than those available to the Gramineae: they are now found especially on mountains and to a lesser extent on sea coasts.

Tillaea is sometimes looked upon as an oddity in the Crassulaceae but, far from being an oddity, it is an essential link with the evolutionary history of the family—indeed, if it did not exist, it would have been necessary to postulate the former existence of plants like *Tillaea*. Incidentally, the relationship between *Tillaea* and the Crassulaceae is paralleled by that between *Hydrocotyle* and the Umbelliferae, *Galium palustre* and the Rubiaceae, *Phyllanthus fluitans* and the Euphorbiaceae, and many others.

6. Santalales and Rafflesiales

It was mentioned previously that some ancestors of the higher plants probably escaped from swamp forest to moss forest and thence to other habitats. These included the ancestors of the Santalales and Rafflesiales, but their escape was not due to adaptation to the usual ecological factors but to their hosts as parasites. It is likely that they were originally epiphytes and, judging by the extreme specialisation of their descendants, acquired the potential for parasitism, if not actual parasitism, very early in their history. Some of them, notably *Rafflesia*, remained in moss forest, but others moved out principally to all the warmer parts of the world, though *Myzodendron* occurs on *Nothofagus* in Tierra del Fuego, and *Viscum* on various trees in Scandinavia.

7. Liliaceae

The Liliaceae would appear to have emerged as perennial bog plants on the fringes of warm temperate swamp forest. They migrated from there to a variety of drier habitats and in so doing proliferated greatly to give rise to about 3,500 species. However, the moist habitat of their early evolution made it unnecessary for them to develop xylem vessels except in the root system. This set a limit to the amount of change that could take place so that, although numerous species were formed, many are minor variations on the same theme. Some (for example, *Narthecium*) remained bog plants, a few (*Petrosavia*) adopted saprophytism, and a few (*Astelia*) became epiphytes rooted in accumulations of humus. Many naturally became rhizomatous (*Convallaria*) or bulbous (*Endymion*) perennial herbs, rooting in the humus of woodland floors. The rhizomatous and bulbous habits were apparently easily acquired and led to a further remarkable colonisation of more open and dry or even desert habitats, in which aestivation is usual (as in *Tulipa*). Relatively few adopted the alternative strategy of xeromorphism by succulence (as in *Aloe*).

THE GEOGRAPHY OF THE HIGHER PLANTS

In the course of history, widely different views have been expressed concerning the original home of the higher plants and how different groups have spread from there to provide the patterns of distribution seen today.

As long ago as 1853, Hooker, after journeying to New Zealand, was inclined to suppose that the southern floras had been acquired by migration from the northern hemisphere. On the other hand, Croizat (1958) proposed that the higher plants had evolved in the Southern Hemisphere and then migrated by various paths (such as the African, Polynesian and Magelian 'gateways') to the Northern Hemisphere.

If the higher plants evolved from ancestors living in tropical swamp forest the truth may lie somewhere between the two extreme views mentioned above. Subsequent distributions would have been distorted by a general drift northwards of the continents with time, the equator in effect moving southwards relative to them. In the Early Cretaceous when the higher plants were evolving rapidly, the equator would have passed approximately through Mexico, North Africa, Arabia, India and Burma, whereas it now passes through Northern Brazil, Central Africa and Central Sumatra. The configuration of the continents was also different in the Lower Cretaceous Period for South America, for example, was then continuous with Africa.

The factors invoved in the migration from the tropics of any congenitum would be:

—The place and time of its initiation.

—The nature of the congenitum: how closely it was 'tied', for example, to a tropical environment.

—The availability of migration routes of which there are basically three, namely dry lowland, mountain chains, and water in rivers, lakes and swamps.

The availability of migration routes will depend in a complex way on the dispositions of land masses in relation to potential climatic zones. No doubt in due course the geophysicists, geologists and climatologists will be able to provide a time sequence of maps showing suitable environmental data. Present plant distributions and fossil plant distributions could then be superimposed and so bring together the basic information to enable deductions to be made as to how such distributions came into being.

Until such maps are available it is possible to make only guesses or broad generalisations. For example, with regard to the distribution of the Fagales, there must have been suitable mountain chains to conduct some members (*Quercus, Fagus, Betula, Corylus*) from tropical moss forest to the cool temperate zones of the north, and others (*Nothogagus*) to the south of the tropics. Another example is provided by the Bromeliaceae and the Cactaceae. Both these families presumably evolved in Central America and representatives of only one genus of each (*Pitcairnia* and *Rhipsalis* respectively) managed a 'last gasp' migration to Africa before the widening South Atlantic Ocean rendered this impossible.

It is easier to draw conclusions at the level of genera and species since in this case it is possible to make better use of chromosomal data. In the words of Stebbins (1971), "Since effective trends of polyploidy are from lower to higher levels, polyploid complexes are particularly useful for analysing problems of plant geography and phylogeny."

Even with a good set of maps available there will be many doubts and difficulties in deciding what migrated when and where. However, in one respect the process could now be accomplished more easily because, if the Congenitum Theory is accepted, it will not be necessary simultaneously to work out migration routes *and* the way in which the supposed evolutionary tree branched.

PHYLOGENETIC TAXONOMY AND SYSTEMATISATION OF THE HIGHER PLANTS

If the evolution of the higher plants took place by the rapid formation of congenita and constricta, and then by a much slower process of speciation, it follows that phylogenetic taxonomy (as distinct from informational or retrieval taxonomy needed for documentation and identification) will fall into two more or less distinct parts.

One part will be concerned with the inter-relations of congenita, and the other part with divergent descent or speciation within congenita and constricta. In some respects the first may be compared to the determination of how shotgun pellets were packed in a cartridge based on an examination of compression facets, and the second to the determination of the trajectories of the fired pellets in their course to the target. Neither determination is likely to be easy.

PHYLOGENETIC TAXONOMY WITHIN CONGENITA

In the preparation of a phylogenetic classification of the modern descendants within a congenitum it will be necessary to construct a hypothetical cladogram showing the pathways of speciation.

In order to construct such a cladogram, two conditions are essential, namely access to a variety of data (anatomical, ecological, geographical, cytological, etc.) and also an appropriate knowledge or theory to allow the proper use of such data. It was only with the advent of cytogenetic theory, for example, that such studies became feasible.

The construction of satisfactory cladograms can never be an easy matter, and it is natural that most studies to date concern speciation within constricta during the Late Quaternary, rather than changes going right back to the congenitum in the Early Cretaceous. Of the many studies made on constricta some have been on plants of economic importance: some good examples are reviewed by Stebbins (1971, Chapter 6).

THE GROUPINGS OF CONGENITA INTO ORDERS

Much effort has been expended in classical taxonomy in the grouping of Families into Orders. Such Orders are the largest tidy assemblages that can be constructed. The number of left-over or 'orphan' Families (as Cronquist calls them) is kept to a minimum. Historically, much of the incentive for this activity has been to use the Orders to construct the larger branches of a Darwinian evolutionary tree, of which the Families would represent the smaller branches.

The Congenitum Theory requires a different view of the structure of Orders. According to this theory, all congenita or their derivative modern Families are 'orphans', but some have closer collaterals than others, as the following argument would indicate.

It would be expected that, if all the congenita had their origin in the Discriminales not wholly as genetical 'lucky dips' but certainly with an element of chance, their constitutions would have some overlap. The overlap would range from so little that a congenitum would be apparently isolated, to so much that two or more congenita would clearly have some association—the association being collateral however, not derivational.

Much useful work has already been done in the assembling of Orders from Families. The task is now to eliminate notions of the Darwinian tree from the structure of those Orders and to reconstitute them as far as possible as assemblages of collateral congenita. In this connection an application of the Sporoclade Theory will to a certain extent be useful.

It is ironic that modern systems of taxonomy are, to a considerable extent, based on the structure of the gynoecium chosen as something least liable to variation. Yet, on the Sporoclade Theory, the gynoecium is seen to be exceptionally plastic in being subject to expansion, pleiomery and secondary apocarpy.

If the structure of the gynoecium is really of smaller taxonomic importance than hitherto supposed, then secondary characters will become of greater importance, and it will be more acceptable to bring together some diverse Orders and to make regroupings or new Orders from their component Families. For example, it would now be possible to consider the closer association of Tropaeolaceae with Capparaceae; Fumariaceae with Balsaminaceae and Polygalaceae; Moringaceae with Bretschneideraceae and perhaps Paeoniaceae.

THE ASSEMBLING OF ORDERS INTO EVOLUTIONARY TREES

The interest generated in the 19th century by the theory of evolution naturally led to speculation on the phylogeny of the higher plants. It was supposed, (following Darwin) that a phylogenetic tree could be constructed with species as twigs, genera as branches and families as even larger branches. Families would then be grouped into orders and these into still larger groups until the trunk of the phylogenetic tree would be reached in the supposed primitive ancestors of all the higher plants.

Since the fossil record of the higher plants was apparently of little assistance in the construction of phylogenies, recourse was had by Bessey (1915) to a list of putatively primitive characters and rules for the use of such characters in the construction of a phylogenetic system. More recently, Sporne (1954) has used the results of statistical studies on the occurrence of primitive characters to make a quantitative assessment of the primitiveness of families. These studies indicated that the families of the Magnoliales were among the most primitive of the higher plants.

Various phylogenetic trees have been put forward: they commonly have Magnoliales forming the trunk, followed by various branchings and ending in the Tubiflorae as the least primitive plants. Examples are to be found in the opening chapters of Engler (1964).

The flaws in all these phylogenies lie first in the assumption that the families which are assessed as more primitive could or did give rise to less primitive families in the course of evolution, and secondly that evolution took place in a series of derivations which of necessity would be spread over a long period of geological time.

On these grounds it would appear that phylogenetic trees do not properly represent the evolution of the higher plants. This view is reinforced by the Congenitum Theory which proposes that there was rapid simultaneous division of an ancestral group into numerous smaller groups in which evolutionary change took place independently and slowly.

THE DIVISION OF THE HIGHER PLANTS INTO MONOCOTYLEDONS AND DICOTYLEDONS

The division of the higher plants into monocotyledons and dicotyledons was proposed by Antoine Jussieu in 1879, and the number of cotyledons has ever since been accepted as a useful and natural criterion for the separation of two large but unequal groups.

Attempts have been made, however, to combine the monocotyledons and dicotyledons into one evolutionary tree with the trunk forking near the base, the Alismatineae taking one branch (being supposedly ancestral to all the monocotyledons) and the Ranuculales/Magnoliales taking the other (being ancestral to all the dicotyledons).

It is well-recognised that floral trimery, lack of normal secondary growth, parallel veins in the leaves, etc. are associated with monocotyledony, whereas floral pentamery, normal secondary growth and reticulate venation are associated with dicotyledony. The *potentials* for these differences were certainly established *before* flowers, closed ovaries and embryos borne in seeds came into existence.

Whether the differences were incorporated into two distinct and separately inbreeding populations (corresponding perhaps to two good species) or whether the differences were incorporated into various races within one population is open to discussion. The fossils of the Sphenophyllales do vary considerably in internal structure and number of leaves per whorl, so presumably their collaterals could have varied similarly. However, as far as the formation of congenita is concerned, the two alternatives would both have yielded similar results.

The important distinction between the two types would not have been in their breeding behaviour but in their different constitutions which directed some ancestors towards monocotyledony and some to dicotyledony. It is here suggested that the different constitutions could have been due to the presence or absence of a group of closely linked genes (a supergene) with pleiotropic effects. Loss of the supergene could have arisen by chromosome breakage and hence unequal partition at meiosis or by the non-disjunction of chromosomes in irregular meiosis with the formation of aneuploids. Such a loss could have occurred independently several times over in plants growing in different places or at different times.

An examination of the chromosome numbers of modern plants shows how extensive aneuploidy and other irregularities have been. Although the resulting numbers are so irregular as to make generalisations difficult and conclusions extremely tentative, there is perhaps a faint indication that 10 and its multiples are relatively more frequent in monocotyledons and 8 and its multiples in dicotyledons.

If $2n = 10$ was the number of chromosomes in the common ancestor and aneuploidy was the cause of the loss of the supergene, some congenita would have received 2n = 10 without loss and some would have received 2n = 8 after loss of the chromosomes bearing the supergene. Loss of such chromosomes could have unlocked extra variability, and the use of this variability could have been enhanced by polyploidy to 2n = 16. The latter is a common number in dicotyledons and one which may account for the greater variability, invasiveness and overall success of the dicotyledons compared with the monocotyledons. It would also account for the greater tendency of monocotyledons to retain a hydrophytic character and various other features such as non-acquisition or partial acquisition of xylem vessels associated with that character.

According to the Congenitum Theory, all congenita, whether they incorporated the restricting supergene or not, would develop in parallel in those features (closed ovaries, embryo sac, double fertilisation) common to the higher plants and not affected by the supergene.

Although the resulting congenita and derivative families can be classified as Monocotyledons and Dicotyledons, with or without the implication of completely separate origin, it should be noted that groups such as the Ranunculales do lean somewhat to monocotyledony. This might be due to the fact that the component genes of a supergene are not absolutely inseparable: a few examples of cross-association of characters (or incomplete syndrome) could almost be expected.

THE HIGHER PLANTS IN THE CONTEXT OF THE PLANT KINGDOM

In this work so far only two groups, namely the higher plants and their possible ancestors the collaterals of the Sphenophyllales, have been discussed. These groups should now be put into the context of the other members of the plant kingdom. They are shown in the timechart presented on the following page:

The sporangia-bearing structures of the Sphenophyllales were cladodes borne in the axils of bracts. It would be reasonable to assume, therefore, that their ancestors arose from plants which bore sporangia on their stems. The Psilophytales and the Psilotales both come into this category, though most of their structures would suggest that they were collaterals rather than in the direct line of descent. A further projection backwards to algae of the structure of the Charales is a still more interesting possibility.

The Calamitales are somewhat closer collaterals of the Sphenophyllales, and are particularly interesting in that *Palaeostachya* shows in its peltate sporangiophores the first manifestation of the tendency towards the rolling of sporoclades: the individual sporoclades can thus be looked upon as the most primitive flowers yet discovered. The Equisetales would be collaterals or derivatives of the Calamitales: their sporoclades are, however, not subtended by bracts.

TIMECHART OF THE SPHENOPHYLLALES
AND THEIR POSSIBLE COLLATERALS

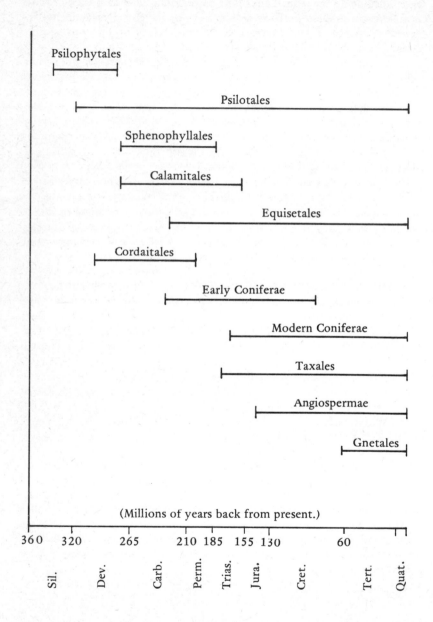

Further collaterals would include the Cordaitales and the Early Coniferae (Lebachiaceae, Volziaceae and Cheirolepidaceae). In all of these the bracts of the female strobili bore secondarily proliferated sporoclades in their axils and they were therefore theoretically capable of progression towards flowering plants. The Cordaitales died out in the Permian, and the Cheirolepidaceae in the Upper Cretaceous. Presumably they were too specialised to achieve congruity with a changing world.

It is here postulated that the same collaterals of the Sphenophyllales which gave rise to the higher plants could also have given rise to the Modern Coniferae, the ovuliferous scale of their cone being interpreted as a branch structure in the axil of the bract scale. The cone of the Modern Coniferae is taken to be homologous with the strobilus of *Sphenophyllum* and *Equisetum,* with the catkin of *Fagus* and the flower of *Magnolia* (the sporoclades of *Equisetum* and their equivalent stamens and ovaries of *Magnolia* being bractless).

It is further postulated that the Modern Coniferae were derived, not from the Early Coniferae, but from generalised small plants which later differentiated and developed to become a dominant tree flora. The generalised small plants have died out, but some idea of them is possibly given by *Dacrydium laxifolium* of New Zealand which grows to a height of about 10cm. with the habit of an *Empetrum.*

Whether any of the higher plants, for example the Fagales, should be associated with the Modern Coniferae is open to question. Perhaps the similarities between them with regard to mycorrhiza and pollination arose out of parallel histories.

The Taxales must now be considered. Their fossils appear in the Upper Triassic and so would appear to antedate those of the higher plants, and would be nearer to the Modern Coniferae.

My interpretation of the male reproductive structure of the Taxales is that what is called the 'flower' is homologous with the male cone of the Coniferae, the strobilus of *Sphenopyllum* and the flower of *Magnolia.* Each peltate 'stamen' of the 'male flower' is formed from a male sporoclade (borne in a bractless strobilus). What would have been once a female cone has been reduced so that only one or two bracts have a flower in the axil. It is possible to carry the interpretation further and suggest that the female flower is formed by proliferation of a female sporoclade but without the formation of an ovary.

In the Gnetales, the flowers of *Ephedra* and *Gnetum* are simple and are derived from single sexual sporoclades. In *Gnetum* the male strobili terminate in a whorl of barren female flowers; this structure suggests how a bisexual flower might be formed by simplification from the whole strobilus (after the manner of the flower of *Euonymus.*) In *Welwitschia,* however, the development of the flowers is already very much along the lines suggested for many of the higher plants. The sporoclades in the axils of the bracts of the original strobili (cones) have undergone some proliferation into secondary strobili which have become converted into flowers. The male flower consists of an axis bearing a pair of bracteoles, a pair of barren male sporoclades, a pair of fertile male sporoclades each bearing three stamens, and a terminal barren female sporoclade. The female flower consists merely of a pair of bracteoles which subtend a single ovule (the structure being somewhat similar to that of *Taxus* mentioned above). The bracteoles develop with the ripening seed (after the manner of those of *Myrica*.)

The fossil record of the Gnetales post-dates that of the higher plants, but, in view of the scarcity of the Gnetales, it would not be surprising, if fossils ever became available, to find that they should prove to be contemporary.

If the interpretations of the reproductive structures of the Taxales and Gnetales are correct, it means that sporoclades occur and flowers have been formed from them in three modern groups and possibly at different times. This would be readily explainable if some small and insignificant collaterals of the Sphenophyllales had existed from the Lower Carboniferous up to the Early Tertiary, a period of over 200 million years, and had split off different groups at successive times.

If, as has been suggested in discussing the origin of the higher plants, the Sphenophyllalean collaterals were hydrophytes they would have retained a simple structure and could have given rise to more complex land plants from time to time. Even if they existed over long periods, their small size and lack of lignified tissue would be contrary to the preservation of recognisable fossils, especially if they, unlike some members of the Charales, were free of calcareous deposits. Consideration of the evolutionary history of the higher plants suggests, in fact, that they evolved under acidic conditions and that many, in their transition from water to dry land, were bog or acid-humus plants.

The advent of the Gnetales is particularly interesting since the component families do not occupy the same kinds of habitats. The Gnetaceae presumably evolved in or near forest, and the Ephedraceae and Welwitschiaceae in or near salt marsh. This parallelism with the higher plants leads to a question which has been asked before and never satisfactorily been answered, namely whether there is an evolutionary association between the Gnetales and the higher plants.

The Gnetales could not be incorporated into the Darwinian evolutionary tree of the higher plants, but they could be accepted according to the Congenitum Theory as somewhat distant collaterals of the higher plants. Whether the higher plants, the Taxales and Gnetales form three separate collateral groups, or whether the Taxales and Gnetales should be regarded as collaterals of certain groups within the higher plants is open to speculation.

If the latter notion is correct, it would be necessary to suggest which groups within the higher plants could be involved. Some suggestions are as follows:

Taxales   Santalales or Laurales, on general woody habit and 'primitive' features of wood and flowers.

Ephedraceae   Casuarinaceae and Chenopodiaceae (*Haloxylon* and *Salicornia*) on superficial morphology. Celastraceae (*Psammoya* is ecologically similar. *Catha* contains an ephedrine.)

Gnetaceae   Celastraceae (*Celastrus* ecologically and habitally similar.) Piperaceae on features of embryology.

Welwitsehiaceae

      Centrospermae ecologically similar (*Beta* is a good example) and there is some resemblance in the structure of their flowers.

This is not an impressive list. Nevertheless, the Gnetales as relictual very early collaterals of some of the higher plants would make them easier to comprehend than as a small isolated and diverse group.

The association of the Gnetales with the higher plants would also be satisfactory in that the vegetative morphology of *Ephedra* is, superficially at least, extremely suggestive of a relationship with the Sphenophyllales.

Many will no doubt find the juxtaposition of gymnosperms and angiosperms uncomfortable or unacceptable. Yet the case that can be made for the incorporation of the Gnetales, and possibly also the Coniferae, into the Higher Plants, is somewhat similar to the case which has been made (and finally accepted) for the incorporation of the supposedly primitive Tupaioidea into the Primates thus bracketing, in the words of Huxley (1863) "the crown and summit of animal creation" (*Homo*) with the "lowest, smallest, and least intelligent of the placental mammals", (*Tupaia*).

It was suggested in Chapter 1 that the emergence of only a few new domains in the course of evolution would be sufficient to account for the history of the higher plants. It is now possible to make some approximate identification of those domains. They are given in the following sequence, which covers a period of possibly 400 million years.

1. Green Alga. This was, or presumably would have become, filamentous. It would have been the gametophyte generation.

2. Charalean type alga. This would have developed the vegetative body as diploid sporophyte. The possibility of this development is indicated by the occurrence of such diplobionts as *Cladophora* of the Green Algae, and of *Chara nitida* in the Charales. It is possible that the modern Charales are those whose ancestors did *not* become diplobionts and were thereby deprived of the possibility of further change.

3. Vascular cryptogam of the level of organisation of the Psilophytales, either a member of that group or perhaps more likely a collateral. *Zosterophyllum*, a submerged water plant with emergent shoots bearing sporangia would suggest a suitable structure.

4. Sphenophyllalean type vascular cryptogam. This semi-aquatic would have developed heterospory and, following the retention of megaspores and zygotes on the parent plant, would have become gymnospermous (but with embryoless seeds).

5. Discriminalean gymnosperm. This semi-aquatic would have developed closed ovaries and seeds with an embryo, thus becoming angiospermous. It also developed an internal organisation and external morphology which facilitated the colonisation of dry land.

COMPARISON OF THE HISTORY OF THE HIGHER PLANTS WITH THAT OF THE MAMMALS IN GENERAL AND MAN IN PARTICULAR

If the proposed theoretical basis for the evolution of the higher plants is truly applicable to them, some part of it at least is also likely to be applicable to other groups of plants and also to animals, for there is no *a priori* reason why their behaviour should have been fundamentally different.

The allantoic placental mammals or Placentalia, for example, are like the higher plants in that, soon after their appearance in the Cretaceous Period, they diversified and very rapidly occupied most of the world.

If it is held that the Congruity Theory of Evolution is of general application, it would be relevant to the evolution of the Placentalia. It is possible that something similar to the Discrimination Theory would also apply to them. Certainly in their evolution some means of prevention of rejection of parasitism of the offspring on the female parent was necessary to allow implantation of the placenta. At the present time there is immune reaction suppression at the junction between the uterus and the placenta. It can be postulated that suppression in the early history of the Placentalia allowed successful wider hybridisation by protecting embryos which would otherwise have been rejected as 'foreign'. Wider hybridisation would have allowed an outburst of variability just as in the higher plants.

The formation of congenita and subsequent parallel evolution would have followed the same pattern as in the higher plants. It would seem, too, that polyploidy in the formation of constricta also took place, for it is otherwise difficult to explain the origin of the present high numbers of chromosomes in the Placentalia, whether considered as absolute or as relative to those of the Marsupalia.

It is possible, of course, that the numbers in the Placentalia are higher partly because the Marsupalia have a countdown mechanism through trisomy in the sex chromosomes (Sharman and Barber, 1951) but, even so, the high numbers have still to be explained: $2n = 66$ for *Equus przewalskii* and $2n = 46$ for *Homo sapiens* are still quite high numbers compared with, say, $2n = 10 + XY_1Y_2$ (in the male) for *Potorus tridactylus*. It should be noted in passing that the reduction in chromosome numbers in Marsupalia leads to the equivalent of speciation in the higher plants.

Polyploidy was presumably easily attainable in the early history of the Placentalia. Sex determination would have been less influential in precluding the survival of polyploids, probably because sexual differentiation was then controlled by autosomal genes (as it is in some modern dioecious polyploid plants). This would also be in keeping with the reversal of sex determination which took place in the evolutionary step from Reptilia (female heterozygous) to Placentalia (male heterozygous). Such flexibility would also suggest that sexual dimorphism was minimal until well after the formation of constricta. It would seem a reasonable hypothesis that subsequent attainment of sexual dimorphism (and its concomitant, mating discrimination) led to mutual recognition and preferred mating within inbreeding groups and hence to speciation.

Fossil apes are known from the Lower Oligocene (about 50 million years ago), so that the formation of their constrictum would have long antedated them, perhaps to the end of the Cretaceous or beginning of the Tertiary. Since that time, the constrictum has given rise to the 'Superfamily' Hominoidea comprising the 'Genera' *Homo, Gorilla, Pan, Pongo and Hylobates* (in a process which, in botanical terms, would be termed speciation. It is not yet known whether *Homo sapiens* is a good species, and it cannot be known whether any of the fossil specimens attained that rank.).

It follows that the commonly accepted phylogenetic classification (Simpson, 1945) shown below could probably be much simplified.

Order PRIMATES
    Suborder PROSIMII
        Infraorder LEMURIFORMES
            Superfamily TUPAIOIDEA
                    LEMUROIDEA
                    DAUBENTONIOIDEA
        Infraorder LORISIFORMES
        Infraorder TARSIIFORMES
            Superfamily TARSOIDEA
    Suborder ANTHROPOIDEA
            Superfamily CEBOIDEA
                Family CEBIDAE
                      CALLITHRICIDAE
            Superfamily CERCOPITHECOIDEA
                Family CERCOPITHECINAE
                      COLOBINAE
            Superfamily HOMINOIDEA
                Family HOMINIDAE
                    Genus HOMO
                Family PONGIDAE
                    Subfamily PONGINAE
                        Genus GORILLA
                          PAN
                          PONGO
                  Subfamily HYLOBATINAE
                    Genus HYLOBATES

The evolutionary diagram of *Homo* put forward by Le Gros Clark (1959, p.47) would, on this basis, need revision, and a re-interpretation of zoological data and the fossil record would be desirable. The considerations which have been detailed above as applying to the Hominoidea would also apply to other groups in the Placentalia.

It is likely that evolution within *Homo sapiens* has long been based on the extended family and its derivative, the tribe, as shown by the patterns of recorded history. Inter-tribal rivalry probably led to the development of intelligence (learning and anticipation) as an offensive and defensive weapon, and this in turn promoted evasive migration. Migration was followed by proliferation giving rise to groups of tribes. A consequence of migration is ecotypic selection, which has modified, for example, shape and stature, skin colour, ability to fatten rapidly on carbohydrate, tolerance to low salt intake (as in New Guinea), tolerance of night chilling, and resistance to local pathogens. Ecotypic selection superimposed on tribal variability provides the distinguishing features of human 'races'. Whatever the type or types of selection which gave rise to races, the intensity has not been great enough to result in heterosis following outcrossing. Currently, tribal and racial barriers are being broken and replaced by the substitute barriers of geographic boundaries, religion and politics—almost anything will serve the psychological need. However, tribalism will presumably again prevail following the depletion of the world's material resources, the reckless exploitation of which has temporarily promoted some degree of outbreeding.

It was mentioned in Chapter I that the sequence of ARGAP's in the evolution of the mammals is likely to be as short as that for the higher plants. Further, the parallel in the animal kingdom to the evolution of the higher plants from a small and insignificant collateral of the Sphenophyllales, would be the evolution of the vertebrates from as yet unidentified aquatic worm-like Palaeozoic chordates. Following the acquisition of a suitable ARGAP, some of these would have given rise to fishes. Others would have avoided predation in the aquatic habitat by moving to intermittently submerged protected habitats (seaweed beds, sands, wet rocks) and then to swamp and dry-land vegetation. In this process of diversification, segregation into congenita would have taken place: those of the future 'Reptilia' would have occupied the more saline habitats and those of the future 'Amphibia' the less saline or fresh-water habitats. Some of the congenita flourished and then died out after exploiting a further variety of habitats, as exemplified by the Ichthyosauria, Rhynchosauria and Pterosauria. Others survived to provide the modern Ophidia, Crocodilia, etc. In one congenitum of therapsid reptiles, a new ARGAP led to the diversification of the mammals and, in due course, to mankind. The delay in the appearance of fossils (such as those of Ophidia in the Tertiary) until long after the establishment of their congenita would merely reflect the fact that, until the descendants of the initially small and insignificant members of the congenitum attained a relatively large size and became abundant in a habitat favourable to the preservation of their remains, their fossils, if any, would be unrecognisable.

REFERENCES

Anderson, E. (1939). Recombination in species crosses. Genetics 24: 668 - 698.

Arnold, C.A. (1947). An introduction to palaeobotany. McGraw Hill, New York.

Axelrod, D.I. (1952). A theory of angiosperm evolution. Evolution 6: 29 - 60

Bessey, C.A. (1915). The phylogenetic taxonomy of flowering plants. Ann. Mo. Bot. Gard. 2: 109 - 164.

Bews, J.W. (1927). Studies in the ecological evolution of the angiosperms. New Phytologist 26: 1 - 21, 65 - 84, 129 - 148, 209 - 248, 273 - 294.

Clark, W.E. Le Gros. (1959). The antecedents of man. Edinburgh Univ. Press.

Croizat, L. (1958). Panbiogeography. Caracas.

Cronquist, A. (1968). The evolution and classification of the flowering plants. Nelson, London.

Darwin, C. (1875). The origin of species by means of natural selection. (6th ed.) Murray, London.

Darwin, C. (1874). The descent of man. (2nd ed.) Murray, London.

Darwin, C. (1879). More letters of Charles Darwin, Vol. 2. (Ed. F. Darwin, 1905) Murray, London.

Dobzhansky, T. (1941). Genetics and the origin of species. New York.

Eames, A.J. & MacDaniels, L.H. (1947). Introduction to plant anatomy. McGraw Hill, New York.

Engler, A. (1964). Syllabus der Pflanzenfamilien. Gebruder Borntraeger, Berlin.

Goethe, J.W. von (1790). Versuch die Metamorphose der Pflanzen erklaren.

Good, R. (1964). The geography of the flowering plants. Longmans Green, London.

Hooker, J.D. (1853). Introductory essay on the flora of New Zealand. London.

Hutchinson, J. (1960). The families of flowering plants. Oxford Univ. Press.

Huxley, J. (1942). Evolution, the modern synthesis. Allen & Unwin, London.

Huxley, T.H. (1863). Man's place in Nature.

Le Maout, E. & Decaisne, J. (1876). A general system of botany. Longmans Green, London.

Melville, R. (1962). A new theory of the angiosperm flower. Kew Bulletin, Vol. 16, No. 1 & Vol. 17, No. 1.

Seward, A.C. (1931). Plant life through the ages. Cambridge Univ. Press.

Sharman, G.B. & Barber H.N. (1952). Multiple sex chromosomes in the Marsupial, *Potorus*. Heredity 6, 345 - 355.

Simpson G.G. (1945), the principles of classification and the classification of mammals. Bull Amer. Mus. Nat. Hist., 85, I.

Sporne, K.R. (1971). The mysterious origin of flowering plants. Oxford Univ. Press.

Stebbins, G.L. (1971). Chromosomal evolution in higher plants. Arnold, London.

Thomas, H. Hamshaw (1958). Fossil plants and evolution. Journ. Linn. Soc., Bot. 56: 129.

Willis, J.C. (1922). Age and area. Cambridge.

INDEX

ERRATA.

p. 19, penultimate line: *For* **ARGAP's** *read* **ARGAPs**

p. 24, line 13: *For* climes *read* clincs.

p. 29, penultimate para: Omit duplicate phrase.

p. 52, Note 6, line 3: *For* Stamonodes *read* Staminodes.

p. 63, *Iris*, line 3: *For* single female *read* single male.

p. 78, Timechart: scale to be moved a little to the left.

p. 82, line 4: *For Chara nitida read Chara crinita.*